The Volcanoes from Puebla

The Volcanoes from Puebla

Kenneth Gangemi

Marion Boyars · London · Boston

Published simultaneously in Great Britain
and the United States in 1979
by Marion Boyars Publishers Ltd.
18 Brewer Street, London W1R 4AS
and Marion Boyars Publishers Inc.
99 Main Street, Salem, New Hampshire 03079

Australian distribution by Thomas C. Lothian
4-12 Tattersalls Lane, Melbourne, Victoria 3000

© Kenneth Gangemi 1979

Library of Congress Cataloging in Publication Data
Gangemi, Kenneth.   The Volcanoes from Puebla
1979   78–70985   7903   781002

ISBN 0 7145 2577 4

Printed in Canada by The Hunter Rose Company

For Jana
1938-1976

Acknowledgements

To Stanford University, where work was done on the manuscript during the time I held a Stegner Fellowship. To the Biblioteca Publica of San Miguel de Allende, with its fine collection of books about Mexico. To P.E.N. American Center, for a small but well-timed grant. To the New York Public Library. To the scores of people, too numerous to mention here, who told me of places to visit, books to read, and people to see.

List of Sections

Acapulco

All over Mexico I consistently heard unfavorable opinions about Acapulco from other Americans. It was as though they were describing a border town. I cannot understand this feeling. I have been to Acapulco twice, and each time have enjoyed myself immensely.

The most important thing in Acapulco, as I see it, is to be content with your hotel. It can be located downtown, near one of the beaches, or up in the hills. I strongly prefer the downtown location, where most things are. I think it is a big disadvantage to be staying elsewhere. The beaches are only a short bus ride away.

The last hotel I stayed in was less than two blocks from the Zócalo. It was clean and freshly painted, and I liked it very much. There was a patio filled with tropical plants, a huge mango tree, and birds in cages. There was even a balcony outside my room with a good view. I was the only American staying in the hotel.

Except for one old man, the hotel was run and staffed entirely by women. They were very friendly and paid a lot of attention to me, even fussed a little bit. It was nice, I appreciated it. At night I liked to sit on the little balcony outside my room and look at the fine view, which included the rooftops of the town and the ring of lighted hills that surround Acapulco Bay. I was very happy in this hotel. And it was ten pesos less than I usually paid in other parts of Mexico.

Acapulco is not just a beach town but also a port and commercial center. The racial mixture is interesting. I saw more black Mexicans there than in any other part of the country, and also many people of various Oriental background. The downtown area is lively at the right times. It is a fine place to walk around during the early morning, when there is shade, before it becomes too hot. Inexpensive cafes, *torta* shops, seafood bars, *jugo* stands, and small restaurants were abundant in the neighborhood of my hotel. *Ensalada de frutas* and sliced mangoes were also sold in several places in the downtown area.

The last time I was in Acapulco I found a good air-conditioned bar in the downtown area, totally Mexican, with a bartender who made delicious tequila sours. It was an American-style bar but for some reason there were mostly middle-class Mexicans there and very few Americans. I liked to go to this bar after my evening walk along the *malecón*, after the sun had set and it was almost dark. It was a good time. The bar was lively and filled with people. Tasty snacks were served during this cocktail hour and dishes of salted *pepitas* were on the bar. I would have a couple of ice-cold tequila sours and become relaxed and happy.

In Acapulco I enjoyed riding the ferry to the good beach on the little island of La Roqueta; swimming with mask, flippers, and snorkel, looking down at bright-colored tropical fishes; riding the motorcycle along the beach areas, and up and around the hills, during the day and night; running along Revolcadero beach, which is straight and uncrowded; walking in the warm air along the *malecón* during the evening and at night; and of course swimming and sunning at the fine beaches, all of which are different. There are many Acapulcos, for all types of people. I like the one that I know.

Aesthete

When I lived in Mexico City I became friendly with a European artist, a man in his early forties. He spoke five languages, had traveled all over the world, and was very knowledgeable of Mexico, especially the social customs. I had many interesting and informative talks with him.

His entire life was centered around art and eventually I came to regard him as an aesthete. Since I was twenty-four at the time he was probably the first aesthete I ever knew. I thought about this man often in Mexico City, questioning his perspective and sense of values. I gradually came to reject them.

In my opinion he overvalued art, to the extent that he usually chose it over life. I think that responding to life firsthand is a higher-order experience than responding to art. What painting can match the sight of a beautiful Mexican child? What cathedral can match the view of the tropical lowlands from the crest of the Sierra Madre?

My European friend and I were very different. I loved to walk on the streets of Mexico City, but he haunted the galleries and museums. He had also visited every significant ruin in Mexico. In general I responded to present-day Mexico and the people, while he responded to Mexican history and art.

He told me a story I will never forget. One time his ship stopped for three hours in Lisbon, a place where he had never been. What did he do? He took a taxi, rushed through the best museum in Lisbon, and then took a taxi back to the ship.

Aguas

These are the least expensive beverages in Mexico, and probably the most delicious. They are very simple: crushed-up fruit and juice, much ice, some water, and perhaps a little sugar. They are usually dispensed with a ladle from large glass jars. I sometimes had *aguas* at taco stands and in *loncherías* when I was tired of beer or soda pop.

Aguas were colorful and appealing to look at in those big jars filled with ice. Nevertheless I had mixed feelings about them. They were far superior to bottled soft drinks, but were sometimes made with contaminated water, and drinking them was a risk. My favorite *aguas* were made from cantaloupes or watermelons. When they were made right and properly chilled, they were delicious.

Alarma!

At the time I lived in Mexico, the leading scandal magazine was *Alarma!* It was very popular and I saw it being read everywhere. I never looked at such magazines in the United States, but for some reason I did in Mexico. Partly it was because they were prominently displayed and the lurid photos caught my eye. Looking at *Alarma!* was also a one-minute Spanish lesson. I rarely held a copy in my hand or got beyond the front page. But I always paused at the magazine stands, most often on the busy streetcorners of Mexico City, to look at the arresting photos and read the headlines and captions.

Alarma! and its imitator *Alerta* often featured morgue photographs of murder victims, juxtaposed with photos of the living murderers. They also juxtaposed photos of people when they were alive with photos of their dead faces. Suicides of young people were a favorite subject, especially those who had hanged themselves. I still remember a poignant photo of a teenage girl who had stepped out of her shoes first.

A typical headline in *Alarma!* was "Fourteen Murders in the Huasteca." One time I saw a photo of a wistful-looking little man; then the caption said that he had killed five of his six children with a machete. Another headline was "He Kills His Old Wife to Be with a Young Girl," with photos of the three of them. A gang-rape story was headlined "The Night Ends in Misery for the Romantic Señorita."

I was interested in the comments, denunciations, and moral judgements that often followed the headlines in *Alarma!*, such as: The Scoundrels! . . . . Depraved! . . . . A Madman! . . . . The Beasts! . . . . Horrible! . . . . An Outrage! . . . . The Vultures! . . . . A Monster! . . . . Incredible!

I remember a story about Mexican soldiers who were searching passengers on a rural bus, looking for weapons being smuggled to guerrillas. The outraged headline read: "Soldiers Touch Women in Their Intimate Parts!" For me, reading this in Spanish (*Partes Íntimas*) on a busy streetcorner in Mexico City, it was unreal. The most memorable headline of all in *Alarma!* was this: "He Screws His Daughter's Dead Body, Then Lends It to a Friend!"

Amecameca

Amecameca is a town about forty miles southeast of Mexico City. It is located at an elevation of over 8000 feet, at the base of the volcanoes Ixtaccíhuatl and Popocatépetl. The volcanoes and the national park on the slopes are generally considered to be a day trip from Mexico City. But to avoid the traumatic experience of leaving and then re-entering the capital on a motorcycle all in one day, I took a better route. I went to the volcanoes while staying in Cuernavaca, with a stop each way in warm, subtropical Cuautla. This route is by far the easiest and most enjoyable.

The market in Amecameca was sunny and bustling with people when I arrived. The sun was very bright at the high elevation, but it was still quite cool. Most of the people wore sweaters or serapes. In the market I bought a pair of mittens, hand-knitted with coarse wool, for about sixty cents. I still have these mittens and use them every winter. They are very durable and will probably outlast the wearer.

A road leads from Amecameca through pine forests up to the saddle between the two volcanoes. The meadows in the pine forests are inhabited by a tiny rabbit called a volcano rabbit, a unique species that is found nowhere else in Mexico. The road ends near the Pass of Cortez. It is at an elevation of about 12,000 feet and is the highest I have ever been on the motorcycle. Through this historic pass came Cortez and his men in 1519. General Winfield Scott led a small American army through the same pass in 1847.

The volcanoes are often obscured by clouds, but I was lucky that day and the weather was excellent. Popocatépetl and Ixtaccíhuatl were lofty and impressive, with their snow-covered peaks against the blue sky. A mountain climber, a young man from Germany, once told me that Popo is a long but relatively easy climb, with a trail most of the way. After I talked with him I was thinking how the Germans love to climb to the tops of things. If I ever climb Popo I am sure I will find several Germans on the summit.

Americans   Part I

I was usually happy to run into Americans when I traveled in Mexico. It was always a pleasure to speak my native language with someone from my own country. I especially liked meeting the people from all different parts of the United States. Nevertheless it is too depressing to write about the majority of Americans that I encountered in Mexico. It was the minority that interested me: the individualists, the real travelers, the bright and sensitive people. I remember many of them with great affection.

In one respect I considered these people to be extensions of my own eyes and ears. I usually asked questions of them and elicited opinions of places and phenomena in Mexico. Seldom did I tell people what I thought about the country and what I liked, only if I was asked directly. Most of all I valued those people who told good stories and anecdotes.

Whenever I met another American, I assumed at the start that his values, feelings, sensibilities, and experiences were totally different from mine. That way I was never surprised or disappointed. I became increasingly more aware of the different styles of traveling. The way a person travels tells you a great deal about him. You cannot question it any more than you can his clothes or the way he speaks.

You would think that people from the southwestern states—Texas, Arizona, New Mexico—would be more knowledgeable about Mexico than other Americans. But this is not true at all, often they are only more misinformed. Besides hearing much second-hand information and many horror stories about Mexico, their initial experience is typically limited to the border towns. In addition most southwesterners have grown up in an atmosphere of anti-Mexican prejudice. I came to dislike the way men from Texas often say *Meskins*.

I met a number of Americans in various places who were uncomfortable, physically ill, and unhappy about one thing or another. Yet they all insisted that they loved Mexico. Whenever I met three people traveling together—usually two men and a woman, but sometimes a man and two women—I could not help wondering about the relationships. Who was sleeping with whom? Were they sleeping separately? Could it be a *ménage?*

The Americans who have lived for a long time in Mexico often talk about how good it was in the old days. That kind of talk has some basis, especially in regard to prices, but mostly it is just nostalgia. I met one man who had been away from the United States for so long that he had forgotten the names of some of the states. The Americans who have lived in Mexico for a long time frequently take on some of the characteristics of the Mexicans. For example, time will often mean little to an old Mexican hand. He may promise much but follow through with little. And he may tend to forget dates and appointments.

Decadence has an opportunity to flourish in Mexico. I often observed the decadent—sometimes I was tempted to say degenerate—Americans of all ages who gravitate there. I noticed that these people tended to cluster together, and often on the seacoasts. A large proportion of the retired Americans in Mexico, especially those with few interests and resources, are alcoholics or at least semi-alcoholics. I was only twenty-four when I lived in Mexico and had no drinking problem. But I observed that the longer I lived there, the more alcohol I consumed.

Americans Part II

Whenever I saw obvious Americans, I would usually stand back and watch them along with all the Mexicans. I remember seeing four young men from the University of Texas, possibly football players, as they walked through the market in Mazatlán. They seemed to be twice the size of the Mexicans. Another time I saw two obvious American girls, both tall with long blonde hair, as they walked through the market in Campeche. The notice they attracted was hard to believe, almost everyone paused to look at them.

I remember an American man in a crowded bakery in Tepic, either drunk or crazy, who kept asking in a loud voice for a *watermelon*. There was some nervousness and a few hidden smiles while he was still there. But after he left, the place was filled with hysterical laughter. People were weeping, and I thought one of the salesgirls would giggle to death.

In the diner of the train from Mexico City to Laredo I talked with a retired teacher who lived in Guadalajara. In the United States he would be living at a subsistence level on his small pension and Social Security check, but in Guadalajara he was able to live rather well. My seatmate on the train from Oaxaca to Mexico City was a woman who periodically worked as a secretary in Chicago. She told me she saves up two thousand dollars or so and then lives and travels in Mexico until it runs out. On the train from Mérida I talked with a young man from Boston who was leading a tour of twenty-seven student nurses. I recall that he looked a bit tired.

Mexico is continually being studied by American scientists and their students. I once turned a corner in San Cristóbal and bumped into six archaeologists from Harvard. Another time in Zihuatanejo I had a good talk with a white-haired marine biologist from San Diego; he was an expert on the shorelife of the west coast of Mexico. I recall with pleasure the informal and idiomatic way he spoke. For example, he referred to a species of molluscs as *these fellers;* and in regards to a nearby river mouth, he said "You got a nice mixin' of sea water and river water over there."

In Acapulco I became friendly with an American girl who was waiting for a divorce from her Mexican husband. Together we went swimming at the attractive pool of one of the luxury hotels, where she knew somebody. It had been a brief marriage for her and she was still unhappy. She told me about all the things her Mexican husband would not let her do. One thing I remember is that he would not let her talk with male friends on the street.

It is common for Americans to sit around and exchange horror stories about Mexico. In San Miguel de Allende I once heard of two American girls traveling on the Gulf coast who were held captive and gang-raped by a group of Mexican soldiers. Another story was about an American couple who had lived for years in San Miguel and maintained a house. One day, because of some trumped-up reason and without any kind of hearing, they were given twelve hours by the police to pack and be on the train to Laredo.

Hepatitis was a constant threat and frequently discussed. I heard of Americans who had been ordered by their doctors to stay flat on their backs for six weeks or more. The thought of forced inaction for such a long time is depressing; for an active person it is probably the worst aspect of the disease. And when you have hepatitis you cannot drink. The thought of Mexico without alcohol is even more depressing.

I once witnessed a hilarious argument between an American tourist and a Mexican shopkeeper. It was over a can of motor oil. The angry American kept saying, in his poor Spanish, *"¡Yo rompo su tienda! ¡Yo rompo su tienda!"* That translates to "I break your store! I break your store!" The excited shopkeeper kept replying, in his equally poor English, "You no break my store! You no break my store!"

In Mexico City I knew a grizzled, white-haired civil engineer from Massachusetts who had worked and traveled all over the world. He told me of building roads in Kenya,

9

bridges in Pakistan, airports in Brazil. In Mexico he was working on a dam in the state of Veracruz. I still remember his casual pronunciations of place names like Tegucigalpa; also the way he quickly and precisely called the lines on a map *iso-magnetic* lines. Like most engineers he had language skills that non-technical people do not usually have. Although he was well-paid, he traveled as inexpensively as I did. He figured that the more you spend on travel, the less you get out of it in fun and education.

In a town on the west coast I met a pretty student from the University of Arizona who had flown from Tucson to Puerto Vallarta. She told me that the plane had made stops at Guaymas, La Paz, and Mazatlán. It was a daytime flight, she had a good seat by the window, and the visibility was unlimited. She told me that she had magnificent aerial views during the entire flight.

In the same town I met an American writer who lived there and spent much of his time fishing. He showed me the ingenious fish-smoker he had built, using an abandoned refrigerator and an electric hotplate. A pan of hickory chips on the hotplate created the smoke. The man caught and smoked far more fish than he could eat, so he bartered the rest for food and supplies. He told me that he lived very well in Mexico on about a hundred dollars a month.

Anti-Americanism

On occasion I was asked by tourists in Mexico about anti-Americanism. They definitely felt something in the air, but it was not that. I sometimes encountered anti-*gringo* and anti-imperialist and anti-tourist attitudes, but almost never anti-Americanism. There is a difference. The great majority of Mexicans have too many ties with the United States, too many friends and relatives here, and are too influenced by our culture to be anti-American. Many times I was told by

Mexicans about their relatives in the United States, and often I was shown photographs.

Our major export to Mexico over the years has really been our culture. The influence of American movies alone has had an incalculable effect upon the Mexicans. American popular songs, the originals in English, are very common on the radios, jukeboxes, and speaker systems. American brands are prized beyond belief. For example I could not buy Mexican oil, even the best, for my motorcycle. They always insisted that I use an American oil.

The Mexicans adapt, with remarkable speed, to many of the American ways. I was often amused to observe it. At the time I lived in Mexico, the California-style luxury coffee-shops were beginning to appear in the larger cities. They were very popular with the middle-class Mexicans. Sweatshirts with the names of American colleges and universities were worn by many of the young people. I would hardly be surprised if the Mexicans became wild about ice hockey someday.

Azotea

In the cities of the United States the rooftops of apartment buildings are generally unused. But in Mexico City the rooftops are considered to be valuable space and are used for many purposes. Thousands of persons, mostly students and old people, live on the rooftops in little cubicles called *azoteas*.

I first learned about them when I was looking for a place to live, a furnished room or a small apartment. Every morning I would read the *anuncios* in the Mexico City newspapers. I would clip the likely prospects, arrange the clipped ads in geographical order, and then tape them to cards.

It was a difficult search. I was competing with Mexicans who knew Mexico City, who had friends and relatives, who spoke Spanish fluently. Then one morning I spotted this ad: *Magnífica, amueblada, azotea, señor solo, honorable.* I liked the location, the rent was reasonable, and so I hurried over.

To my delight I found that the little room was just right for me. It was as Spartan as a monk's cell, but with two windows and lots of light. It was completely furnished with a bed, a desk, and bookshelves.

I paid a month's rent to the Señora, received my key and receipt, and then spent the next hour on the sunny rooftop, admiring my new *azotea*. I was very happy. In two directions there were fine views of Mexico City. The rooftop also had a cat, a tiny garden, a pen of rabbits, several chickens, and many pots of flowers. I lived there for three months.

Bach

One afternoon I was taking a long walk in an outlying section of Guadalajara. It was a warm day and after a while I became rather tired. Then I suddenly heard the sound of singing from a small church. I went to the doorway, stepped inside, and stood in the rear for a while. Then I slipped into an empty seat in the back. There were mostly women and children in the church. I listened for a long time to the voices and the music, which I think was Bach. The experience completely transformed my mood, and I left the church refreshed and in high spirits.

Back in the USA

Psychologically I left Mexico several weeks before I actually crossed the border. My heart and mind were already back in the United States. Except for two trips to the border for new tourist cards, I had been in Mexico for over a year. Living there had become a matter of diminishing returns.

I was even tired of traveling in Mexico. After the first impression, a new town meant little to me. Excitement while unpacking in my hotel room was inevitably followed by restlessness one or two days later, and thoughts of moving on.

It was definitely time to go back. There was a period of sadness when I realized that I would soon be leaving Mexico. Then that feeling gradually changed to anticipation and excitement at the thought of returning to the United States.

I crossed the border at Nogales, Arizona, the same place where I had entered Mexico over a year before. U.S. Customs was a pleasant surprise. A gray-haired officer with experienced eyes looked me and the motorcycle over. He asked if I had brought back any liquor, and also the total value of all my purchases. Then he said, "O.K., you can go." No suitcase inspection!

Living in an underdeveloped country brings a new appreciation for certain aspects of the United States. My first impressions, since I was on the motorcycle, were of the automotive culture. In Nogales I noticed the new cars and pick-up trucks. The gasoline stations were clean, the attendants were polite and courteous. They spoke English. I examined the American money with wonder; the coins seemed very small. On the way to Tucson I could hardly believe the excellent roads. They were wide and perfectly paved. What a wealthy country this is, I thought.

In Tucson the differences from Mexico were even more apparent. Americans were everywhere. I delighted in the air-conditioned drugstores and enormous supermarkets. I appreciated the careful and well-mannered drivers. The people all seemed to have new clothing, they looked clean and cool and prosperous. They waited their turn. American newspapers were sold everywhere, the road maps were excellent. Drinking water flowed right from the tap.

The first American food I had was a chef's salad in an

enormous California-style luxury coffeeshop. It had effective air-conditioning. In the spotless men's room I looked with pleasure at the new plumbing fixtures and shining tiles. There was soap, toilet paper, and paper towels. Back at the counter I ran my hand over the clean Formica and gleaming stainless steel. The waitress had blonde hair, and the icewater she brought me was safe to drink. I saw my first pepper shaker in over a year. The paper napkin seemed very large. A plastic-coated menu was printed in English.

(Friends of mine think that my preference for these California-style coffeeshops is perverse. But it is all because of the motorcycle. After an hour or more under the hot sun in the desert, the modern air-conditioned coffeeshop becomes a real oasis. It is the cool refuge from the big sky and the hot sun. In Mexico these places did not exist.)

I had a few items to buy in Tucson, and it was a great luxury to speak English in the stores. Language superiority again! I would often begin to speak Spanish and then stop myself. I quickly discovered, however, certain advantages of Spanish. For example, *nada más* is easier to say than *nothing more;* and *sí* is easier to say than *yes.*

After finishing my shopping, I realized a new appreciation for American-made goods and retailing techniques. This statement will probably only be understood by people who have lived in an underdeveloped country. It was also a pleasure to talk with the Chicanos who work in the stores in Tucson. They look somewhat like the Mexicans, but I had to keep reminding myself that they are Americans and speak English.

The phenomenon of being somewhat estranged from the American culture did not become apparent until weeks later. I also found that I had a new interest in Chicanos and their social and cultural problems. Naturally I missed many things about Mexico. The American children, for example, looked bland and washed-out. They did not seem to be as appealing as the Mexican children. Sometimes in my American city I would think: Where are all the buses? Where are the stands that sell fresh-squeezed orange juice? Where is the *cantina* music? Where is all the free time I had? Where are the plazas?

Bakery

When I lived in the village I would walk to the *panadería* every morning to buy hot rolls for breakfast. It was one of my great pleasures. It was still cool at that hour and I would keep in the sun. I remember the cobblestones, the cool morning air, the white walls in bright sunlight.

At the bakery I would wait in back of a crowd of women and girls. They would be talking quietly in Spanish. I was usually the only man, and some of them turned their heads and simpered and giggled at my presence. When the *bolillos* came from the oven I liked to watch them press together towards the front: the warm females, clothed in soft cottons, pressing breasts against backs and bellies against buttocks.

Barber

In the village there was a barber who cut hair in the small plaza adjoining the market. I sometimes saw him walking to work in the morning. He was a dignified-looking man who carried a folding chair under one arm and a valise in the other. Everything he needed was in the valise. I thought the simplicity of his way of working contrasted greatly with the elaborate barbershops of the United States.

He would set up shop across from the market, often under a tree. Whether he was in sunshine or shade depended upon the temperature and time of day. The folding chair was always facing in the most interesting direction, towards the market. I would sometimes watch him while I was sitting in the small plaza or walking through it. I noticed that he gave many of the older *campesinos* the same kind of short haircut that I prefer.

Beggars

In Mexico I quickly acquired an attitude towards beggars. The feeling of guilt diminished rapidly and eventually almost disappeared. Yeats said it: *Cast a cold eye.* I remember the time in Cuernavaca when I weakened and slipped a child twenty centavos. Immediately three others took his place. What was it? *Charity is like facing a hungry crowd with a single crumb.*

Nevertheless I weakened more times than I like to admit. One time I was eating a strawberry *paleta* or popsicle, and a ragged boy came up to me and asked if he could have a *paleta* too. It was impossible to turn him down. Another time it was a blind old man, led by a small girl with an outstretched palm and accusing eyes. And once I came out of a *tienda* with a liter of milk. I saw two small children who were so skinny and ragged that I just had to give them the milk. I observed that many of the Mexicans give to beggars, but for a variety of reasons. Some of them regard it as a petty bribe to keep from being annoyed.

Bicycle

In Mexico City I was run over by a bicycle. It was a rainy afternoon and I was crossing the street to the bus stop. Bam! The next thing I knew, I was flat on my back in the street. There was no pain, just surprise. You never see the one that hits you. I got up and helped to untangle a teenage boy from his bicycle. He began to cry softly. I think he had a sprained or broken ankle. I needed help, but the six people waiting at the bus stop did nothing. They just looked at us with those deadpan Mexican expressions.

Bishop

When I lived in Mexico City, I found that it was a good base for trips in all directions. An all-day excursion on the motorcycle cost only a small amount for lunch, gasoline, and incidentals. One time I visited the Basilica of Guadalupe on my way to the pyramids at Teotihuacán, as many people do. It was convenient, and the basilica is the best-known religious shrine in Mexico.

But I was not prepared for the depressing scene. It turned my stomach to see those people, some of them seriously ill, walking on their knees across many yards of pavement towards the shrine, hoping they might be cured. I was reminded that Paul Blanshard once wrote that the Roman Catholic Church is a unique blend of personal faith, human compassion, clerical exploitation, and submissive ignorance.

The offical account of the "miracle" of the Virgin of Guadalupe, an absurd tale, is not worth describing here. It is in many guidebooks and histories. But the real story of this "miracle", the thinking behind it, is quite interesting. A clever 16th-century Spanish bishop named Juan Zumárraga engineered it all, a brilliant deception that is still fervently believed by millions of Mexicans today.

I first came across the real story in the writings of a Mexican artist of the thirties, who was a Marxist. James Norman also mentions some interesting aspects of this "miracle" in *Terry's Guide to Mexico*. Besides relics and religious art, I think the Basilica of Guadalupe might also contain a statue of Bishop Juan Zumárraga. It would be a kind of perverse tribute to man's ingenuity in manipulating his fellow man.

Blanket

The village was located on the slopes of one of the volcanoes, at a high elevation where the temperature often dropped below freezing. It had a reputation for good blankets and I had come to buy one. The weaving shop that I visited was one of the largest in the village. I was able to walk around and observe the blanket-making procedure from beginning to end.

I saw the separate piles of raw wool, already cleaned and sorted, with the colors ranging from white to shades of gray and brown to black; the combing and spinning of the wool into coarse yarn; and the actual weaving, with the flying shuttle shooting back and forth across the loom.

When it came time to select a blanket I chose one with only natural colors, and with lots of the dark brown and black wool that I liked. I was very happy with my Mexican blanket, and I still have it. It is heavy and durable and will probably last for a hundred years.

Bohemia

It was mostly in Mexico that I picked up a distaste for the Bohemian games and costumes of the United States. I eventually came to regard it as the second most common type of conformity, but somehow worse than the first. I always felt a little sorry for the young Mexicans who were aping these Bohemian fads and fashions. The name for this cultural phenomenon changes periodically. Whatever you want to call it, it is appropriate to a country like the United States, which is in relative decline. But it does not really have a place in a developing country like Mexico.

Books

My knowledge of Mexico was primarily gained from firsthand experience, but much of it was discovered in books. In the *biblioteca* and in books of my own I read a great deal about Mexico. My motivation was high, for I was living in the country at the same time that I was reading about it. Besides the books mentioned here and in the "Guidebooks" section of this book, there are many others that I skimmed or read in part.

Among the books I can recommend are *The Bernal Díaz Chronicles,* translated and edited by Albert Idell; *Tepoztlán: Village in Mexico* by Oscar Lewis; *The Children of Sanchez* by Oscar Lewis, which is a valuable book, a landmark work in sociology; and *Many Mexicos* by Lesley Byrd Simpson, one of the most readable histories of Mexico.

Barbarous Mexico by John Kenneth Turner is the classic indictment of the dictatorship of Porfirio Díaz. The book has been called the *Uncle Tom's Cabin* of the Mexican Revolution; it is filled with horrifying accounts of slavery and brutality in the Mexico of 1909. *The Wind That Swept Mexico* by Anita Brenner is on the same subject, and has a fine sequence of photographs that depict the history of the Mexican Revolution.

Mexico: The Struggle for Peace and Bread by Frank A. Tannenbaum is an excellent book. I remember that he has a good explanation of why the Indians embraced the Catholic Church so readily. After reading Tannenbaum and learning of the incredible struggles of the people against the land, it is difficult ever to be annoyed by a bad road or a slow train in Mexico. It is remarkable that the road or railbed is there in the first place.

Viva Mexico!, a personal account by Charles Macomb Flandrau, was first published in 1908. It was widely praised, is still a favorite of many readers, and has been reprinted many times. Mostly it is about the time the author spent on a coffee *finca* in the state of Veracruz. Charles Flandrau, a sensitive, intelligent, and observant young man, saw very clearly what Mexico is all about. I specially remember his apt appreciation of the Mexican plaza and its important place in the life of a town. Much of what Flandrau relates is still true today. When I read the book, I was amazed at the similarities between his Mexico of 1908 and the one I know.

Calle Bolivar

The middle-class neighborhoods in Mexico City are pleasant enough, but not very interesting. I would prefer not to live in such a neighborhood. If I were to move back to Mexico City, I would look instead for an apartment near Calle Bolivar. It is one of my favorite streets in Mexico City. Although it is really part of the downtown area, it has a neighborhood feeling. The part of Calle Bolivar that I like is the four blocks between Carranza and the Plaza de Regina. The other cross streets are Uruguay, El Salvador, and Mesones. A number of inexpensive hotels are in the neighborhood, and it is lively, very Mexican, and filled with places to eat.

Calle Bolivar is convenient to public transportation. It is only a short walk to the Zócalo, where the express buses that go down Reforma start out—and where you can be sure of getting a seat. The new buses are fast, cheap, and comfortable. Streetcars run down Bolivar and Uruguay, and the area is crisscrossed by second-class buses. The Metro station is a five-minute walk to the south.

All the attractions of the downtown area are within easy walking distance of Calle Bolivar. The Alameda is only a short walk to the northwest. The San Juan Market, a good place to buy food, is nearby. There is a branch post office at Bolivar and Mesones. San Juan de Letrán, one of the liveliest streets in Mexico City, is only a block away.

Occasionally I awakened early and took walks in this neighborhood at dawn. It is one of my favorite times in

Mexico City. I noticed that Calle Bolivar and the side streets were exceptionally clean in the early morning. During the day, when it is busy and active, Calle Bolivar is a fine place for a random walk. It is stimulating, it teems with noise and people, it has interesting things to see. I enjoyed shopping for my hotel-room snacks in this neighborhood, and trying all the little cafes and fast-food stands.

Cantinas

Cantinas held little interest for me in Mexico. I liked to walk past their swinging doors and smell the *pulque* and hear the mixture of voices from inside. I enjoyed the lively Mexican music that came from *cantinas,* at all hours of the day and night. But I seldom had a desire to go inside.

Cantinas were generally drab and unattractive. They did not allow women. They often had *borrachos* or drunks, hard to get rid of, who sometimes wanted to talk with and perhaps buy a drink for the Americans. It was a mental strain to speak Spanish with a man who was slurring his words. I cannot imagine why a non-Mexican would want to go to a *cantina;* there are much better places to drink in Mexico.

I admit that occasionally I would go into a *cantina* for a quick shot of tequila, when I was in the mood. But I would knock it down fast and then leave, before some *borracho* would start talking to me or try to buy me a drink.

Capitalista

I once had a nice talk with a Mexican businessman who owned a small bus company. He had nine second-class buses, all very old, that served a short route in Guadalajara. Two or three of the buses were always in the shop being repaired, but the others were enough to take care of the route. I remember that the man was exuberant and almost clapping his hands with glee as he talked about the future. Business was good, patronage was steadily increasing, he would soon buy another bus, his company was making lots of money.

Carts

I came to admire and appreciate the carts or *carritos* used by the taco vendors in Mexico. They are highly efficient ways to conduct a fast-food operation. Several times, when business was slow, I had *simpático* taco vendors show me the supply areas of their carts. They were proud of their carts and eager to show me everything. There was a supply of water, just enough to last the day. Cylinders of gas provided fuel for cooking and light for night-time operations. The number and variety of the items that some of the larger carts can contain is amazing. I saw that the supply areas were highly organized, with a place for everything. In Mexico an industrious man can support a good-sized family with such a cart.

Casa

In a Mexican village, a house often appears as a wall facing the street with a door in it. The visitor to Mexico soon learns that everything is behind these walls. Seen from the outside, the *casa* is all defense: rough masonry walls, iron bars over the windows, a heavy door facing the street. But inside a man may be quietly reading in a lovely patio, filled with plants and flowers, exposed to the sun and sky.

My favorite types of houses, and also types of towns, have always been those that originated in the vicinity of the Mediterranean. The words *Mediterranean climate* have always appealed to me. In regards to the design of houses, this climate is a great advantage. For one thing, it makes patios possible. I think the Spanish or Mediterranean patio is nothing less than one of the noblest achievements of man.

Spanish architecture was already well-evolved when it was transported to Mexico. There it was ideally suited for the climate and the building materials available. This graceful and efficient manner of building has survived the Industrial Revolution and all the subsequent technology. I often admired the Spanish or Mexican colonial architecture when I lived in Mexico. It is so simple, elemental, and functional. The exterior walkways and *portales,* for example, that are shaded from the sun: no country with a hot climate has ever improved upon that.

When I lived in the village I came to identify with the *casa* furnished in the Mexican colonial style. It was minimal and suited my ascetic temperament. There was no heating system; it was always cool inside, and sweaters were usually worn. I remember the white walls, the black-painted metal, the inexpensive materials, the wooden beams against the white ceiling, the stone floors with no rugs, the durable furniture of heavy wood. I felt very much at home in those quiet and sparsely-furnished rooms. There was a good feeling of simplicity, restraint, and permanency.

Cathedrals

I have mixed feelings about the insides of churches and cathedrals. I like the architecture, the subdued light, the serenity, the emphasis on the spiritual part of man. But there is much that is offensive to me and I am often reluctant to go inside.

In Mexico I discovered a good use for these archaic structures. An empty cathedral makes a fine refuge and is often the coolest place in town. When taking long walks I would sometimes rest in one during the heat of the after-noon. It was always quiet and peaceful. A ten-minute break in a cool cathedral was a welcome relief from the hot streets and incessant traffic. I liked to compare the difference in myself at the time I entered the cathedral and at the time I left. Those ten minutes usually made a big difference.

Cattle

On my motorcycle trips through the tropical lowlands I picked up an affection for the Brahma breed of cattle. They are highly attractive animals, with fine hides and coloring—the bulls, the cows, and especially the calves with their big floppy ears. Many times I stopped the motorcycle by the side of the road, turned off the ignition, and just looked at them, a few feet away. Naturally they all stopped grazing and looked at *me*.

Ceiling Fans

On my trips in Mexico I came to appreciate the ceiling fan or *ventilador*. It was one of my absolute requirements for a hotel room in hot and humid areas, especially along the Gulf coast. Ceiling fans usually have five or more speeds. They are efficient cooling devices and use relatively little electricity. They also help to keep mosquitoes away. In many ways I prefer ceiling fans to air-conditioners. All the windows in a room with a ceiling fan can be open, whereas the windows in an air-conditioned room must be closed. Ceiling fans are often installed in new hotels in Mexico, so they are certainly not a thing of the past.

Celaya

One afternoon I was sitting in the plaza in Celaya when a group of girls came along and started to skip rope. I watched them for a while. They were girls of different ages, skipping rope in their own individual ways, and having lots of fun. Cute little girls of eight or nine alternated with luscious young females of fifteen or sixteen. I think it is appealing to watch teenage girls skipping rope and enjoying themselves. I appreciated the combination: they had the bodies of young women and the joyous spirit of little girls.

Cerveza

Beer is what the majority of Mexicans drink, far more than *pulque*, tequila, or *mezcal*. And the Mexican beer is excellent. The brands include *Corona, Dos Equiss, Carta Blanca, Superior, Tecate, Pacífico, Leon Negra, Bohemia,* and *Moctezuma*. I had them all. It is odd that none of the guidebooks, in their sections of Spanish phrases, list one of the most important phrases of all: *"Una cerveza, por favor."*

Certain brands are associated with the cities in which they are brewed: *Leon Negra,* for example, with Mérida, and *Pacífico* with Mazatlán. *Victoria* is the cheapest and is often sold in the cafes in the markets. I thought it was drinkable. After a few months in Mexico I sometimes just asked which brand was the cheapest: *"¿Cuál es la marca más barata?"* As long as the beer was cold, I did not really care which brand I was served. They all tasted fine to me. Naturally I had some preferences in label designs and bottle shapes.

Ceviche

Ceviche in Mexico is generally any type of cold seafood marinated with onions, spices, peppers, and tomatoes. It can be made from fish, crab, octopus, conch, abalone, or a combination of these. *Ceviche* is often mediocre, but when it is fresh and made right it is delicious. It goes well with cold beer.

The best *ceviche* I ever had was at a stand-up seafood bar in downtown Mexico City, patronized mostly by businessmen. I went there many times, whenever I was in the neighborhood. They served *ceviche* with a little olive oil, a scoop of avocado, and a squeeze of lime. The best was also the least expensive and most popular, *ceviche de pescado*. They also served shrimp and oyster cocktails, which were delicious. I sometimes had the *Campechana* cocktail, which is a combination of oysters and shrimp. Or the *vuelve a la vida,* which is all types of seafood mixed together.

At this seafood bar I liked to overhear the conversations of the Mexican businessmen who were standing near me. They mostly talked about food, sports, women, politics, and business. My only complaint about the place was the all-male atmosphere. But it was the custom. It is unfortunate that women in Mexico can not know the pleasures of a good seafood bar.

Chichi

Whenever I moved into a hotel room, I changed it around a little to suit myself. I presume everyone does this to some extent. In a hotel in Mérida I ran into a maid who would every day change the room back to its original state. At first I was slightly annoyed at this, but after the third day it became funny.

The maid was a little Indian woman who was probably

about sixty years old. She was not much more than four feet tall, as are many of the Maya women, and always wore a clean white *huipil*. She usually had a little girl with her. I guess the old woman figured that there was a proper order for the room that must always be maintained.

So every morning she changed the room back to its original state. I never said a word to her, but every afternoon I changed it back again. This went on for over a week. We were exceedingly polite to each other in the halls, and were always smiling. There was not a hint of the battle of wills that was taking place.

I often heard the little girl call the old woman *Chichi*. Later I found out that *chichi* is the Maya word for the Spanish *abuela,* which means grandmother. Before I left, I had a conversation with the desk clerk about the old woman. He told me that she had worked at the hotel ever since she had been a young girl.

Chickens

All over Mexico, and most memorably in the tropical villages, I saw chickens running loose near the little houses. They would venture to the edge of the road and into patches of vegetation to look for food. The economics of raising chickens in such an easy and casual manner appealed to me. At the time I lived in Mexico, baby chicks were sold in the market for one peso. A woman could buy ten chicks for ten pesos and bring them to her house. After keeping them in a cage for two weeks or so, she could let them run loose in the yard and find their own food. At least five of the chicks would probably survive to maturity. By that time the woman would have spent the original ten pesos for the chicks and perhaps another ten pesos for chicken feed. The chickens would have foraged for the rest of their food: seeds, insects, vegetation, etc. In the end the woman would have five

chickens—and very tasty ones, because of their varied diet—
that cost her less than two dollars.

Children

It seems that I spent a lot of time looking at small children in
Mexico. They are the most beautiful children I have ever
seen. The little girls were my favorites, with the ribbons in
their hair, their tiny earrings, and their big brown eyes. I
responded to them most of all when they were dressed up on
Sundays, after church and at the *serenata*.

Why are so many of the Mexican children so appealing? I
asked other Americans, who generally agreed with me, but
none of them could put it into words. I think it is partly
cultural, the way the children are dressed and behave. But the
main reason is probably *la raza* itself. I often noticed the
pleasing contrast between the white of the eyes and teeth, and
the tan skin, brown eyes, and dark hair.

I had to be gentle and totally unthreatening with Mexican
children in order to gain their confidence. They are often
afraid of foreigners. Nevertheless small children in Mexico
think nothing of standing a few feet away and staring directly
at a stranger. They are certainly not afraid of making eye
contact.

This often happened to me in *loncherías,* when a child
would wander away from a family table. Whenever I noticed
small children staring at me in such a manner, I was
delighted. I would stare right back. Then I would smile, and
they would smile also.

Little cellophane packets of jellybeans are sold in most
parts of Mexico. I always carried some with me to give to
small children, at times when it was appropriate. The timing
is important. You must present the packet of jellybeans to the
child at just the right moment. I will never forget the looks
on the faces of some of those children when I suddenly
handed them the packet of jellybeans.

Chocolate

One morning when I was walking in Oaxaca I discovered a shop that sold nothing but *chocolate*. I went inside, looked around a little, and observed a woman at the counter. She purchased separate weighings of sugar, cinnamon, and cocoa bean. Then she had it all ground together so she could make *chocolate* at her home.

After she left I had a nice talk with the owner of the shop, a white-haired old man. He was very friendly and told me all about his business. He told me where the *cacao, canela,* and *azúcar* came from in Mexico. Before I left he gave me some raw *cacao* to taste, and also some ground *chocolate*.

Cine

One of the little pleasures of living in Mexico City is walking to the *cine* in the evening along the Paseo de la Reforma, one of the most beautiful boulevards in the world. I always left early so that I could have a long and leisurely walk. The statues and fountains along Reforma are lighted at night, and it is very pleasant.

There were usually lines outside these *cines,* which showed mostly American and European films. In Mexico a line of people is called a *cola* or tail. A man standing behind you will think nothing of giving you little prods in the back to move you along. I remember the first time it was done to me: I turned around and looked back at the man, wondering what the hell was going on.

The *cines* on Reforma are all plush "first-class" theaters, but some of the bourgeois lobbies contain murals with revolutionary themes. I was amused by the contrast. The young people of Mexico City apparently love the *cine* dearly. It provides escape from the Mexican culture and is one of their main contacts with the outside world. I often observed them in the crowded lobbies: affluent teenagers, university students, young middle-class couples. Most of them I would describe as fine-looking young people.

I saw a number of the propaganda shorts made by the Mexican government. They are well-made and very effective. I remember that the American films were usually re-titled to appeal to the romantic notions of the Mexicans. "One, Two, Three" became *Los Peligros del Amor*. "Moon Pilot" became *Mi Novia es del Otro Mundo*. The subtitles in the American westerns, which are extremely popular in Mexico, were often amusing: Gary Cooper asking *"¿Qué pasó, hombre?"* as he bends over a wounded cowboy; and John Wayne sauntering into the chuckwagon circle, waving his hand in greeting, and saying *"Buenas noches, amigos."*

Ciudad Victoria

Americans who live in Mexico, unless they have applied for *inmigrante* status, must periodically travel to the border. They must leave Mexico and then re-enter to obtain new tourist cards and vehicle papers, which are only good for about six months. This fast turnaround is commonly known as a border trip. It is technically illegal, but everyone does it. I made two of them when I lived in Mexico, one to Texas and the other to Guatemala.

My first border trip was to McAllen, Texas. It is a pleasant town in the lower Rio Grande Valley. I spent a day there, purchasing motorcycle parts and a few American-made items. Early the next morning I re-entered Mexico. I planned to spend the night in Ciudad Victoria, a small city about 200 miles to the south. It is the capital of the interesting state of Tamaulipas.

During the month of July it is a long hot ride on a motorcycle from McAllen to Ciudad Victoria. It was late afternoon when I arrived, and the temperature was still above ninety. I was hot, tired, and exhausted. I found a good and inexpensive hotel near the main plaza, selected a nice room, made a smooth check-in, parked the motorcycle in a corner of the lobby, and then went upstairs and took a long shower. I felt much better afterwards: pleasantly tired and sunburned, but clean and refreshed. I lay on the bed for a while and then put on fresh clothing and went out for a walk.

By this time it was early evening, the sky was red in the west, and the cooler air was delightful. Tamaulipas is one of the big orange-producing states in Mexico, and there are stands all over that sell fresh-squeezed orange juice. At one of the curbside stands I watched a teenage girl squeeze the oranges. She was a pretty girl in a cotton dress, with tan skin, perfect teeth, and shining brown hair. In the tropics the girls wear light-weight dresses and their bodies are very evident. She looked eighteen but said she was sixteen. I noticed that her dress was thin and faded from much use and many washings. It was threadbare around the nipple area.

Afterwards I walked around for a while and had a number of little snacks from various stands and vendors. There were many people on the streets, I was in a good mood, and I decided that Ciudad Victoria was a pleasant surprise. When it .became dark I went to sit on a bench in the plaza. It was nice sitting there in the warm air, and I was happy and content. I noticed that the squirrels in the plaza were gray, but that their breasts, bellies, and sides were rust-colored. I had never seen squirrels with such coloring. When I asked a small boy about them, he told me they were called *jardillas*.

Comida

The American traveler in Mexico is well advised to change his eating habits to conform with the Mexican custom. That means a big lunch in the early afternoon and only a snack or light supper at night. In Mexico many of the *loncherías* and *restaurantes* feature a low-priced *comida corrida*. This is a lunch with three or four or five courses, served during most of the early afternoon. I would often plan all other eating for the day around an inexpensive *comida*. It is one of the keys to low-cost travel in Mexico.

The *loncherías* and *restaurantes* usually have small signs or blackboards outside, with the price and description of the *comida*. Sometimes it is only a piece of paper, posted inconspicuously or included with the menu. But it gives all the information. There are often two or three *comidas* with different prices. I usually chose the least expensive one, for it meant less food. My stomach never completely adjusted to having the main meal in the afternoon.

When I discovered a place that served an outstanding *comida,* I would go back again and again. A typical offering might be: *COMIDA CORRIDA/Doce pesos. Sopa del Día. Sopa de Arroz. Pescado Frito o Carne Asada a la Veracruzana o Pollo con Mole. Frijoles Refritos. Papaya o Flan. Café o Té.* I always looked for the words *a la Veracruzana*. It meant a spicy sauce, often delicious, made with onions, peppers, and tomatoes.

Commercial Towns

There are hundreds of towns and small cities in Mexico that rarely see an American tourist. On my motorcycle trips I often spent the night in such towns. They were usually situated on a main highway, but were of ordinary appearance and had little to attract a tourist. They were commercial towns, often farming and ranching centers, with economies of their own. The automobiles with American plates might stop for gasoline, but that was all.

I arrived in such towns expecting little, only a choice of hotels for an overnight stop. But I was surprised on a number of occasions. When walking around that evening or the next morning, I often found that I liked the town very much, usually because it was authentic and unpretentious. And so I stayed another night. It was one of my traveling principles: when I was unexpectedly happy in a place, I changed my plans and stayed there longer.

Some of the towns I would place in this category are Teziutlán, Iguala, Huichápan, Acámbaro, Pichucalco, Ciudad Victoria, Tamazunchale, Navojoa, Zamora, Tuxtla Gutiérrez, Alvarado, Tenosique, Celaya, Magdalena, Zitácuaro, Ciudad Mante, and San Andrés Tuxtla. There are many others in every state in Mexico.

Correo

I heard many horror stories about the mails when I lived in Mexico. The stories were depressing: checks, documents, manuscripts, drawings, photographs, important letters, all lost and gone forever. It happened to me only a few times. But I still wonder about those letters I never received. I still feel anger when I think of the letters mailed that people told me never arrived. Of course the vast majority of mail in Mexico cheerfully arrives at its destination, and almost all the postal workers are honest and diligent.

An American living in Mexico soon acquires a casual attitude about the mail. You send a letter but are well aware that it or the reply may never arrive. The *correo* offices vary widely. I saw many of them because I used *lista de correos* when I traveled. Some offices are brisk and efficient, with a feeling of high morale among the postal workers. But in others the people seem morose, depressed, and positively neurotic.

Lista de correos or general delivery is used much more in Mexico than in the United States. Many Mexicans have no real address, or at least no mail delivery. On my trips to different parts of the country, it was always a thrill to spot my name on the various *listas*. Sometimes I had to look very carefully. It is hard to believe, but many of the postal workers are only semi-literate. Once I found myself listed under the M's as MR Kenneth. An English friend always checked the E listings, for sometimes his letters were filed for Esq.

The worry and insecurity about mail is part of the price one pays for living in Mexico. But you learn to cope with the situation. The longer I lived there, the more letters I sent *registrado*. At least the service is very inexpensive. With *registrado*, they cancel the stamps right in front of you. The speed with which some postal workers do registered mail has to be seen to be believed. Stamp! Stamp! Scribble! Rip! Cancel! Then a *Gracias* and a smile. I always watched where they put the envelope . . . and so did the Mexicans, I observed.

Part of the explanation for the slowness and unreliability of the mails is that the Mexican postal workers are terribly underpaid, and their working conditions are often very poor. I sometimes thought: What would *I* do if I were a Mexican postal worker? Suppose someone in my family was seriously ill, and there was no money for doctors and medicine? Suppose someone would die unless they had an operation? I would probably do the same thing as some of the postal workers: tear the stamps off the envelopes of the *gringos*, throw away the contents, and trade the stamps in for money.

Dentista

I had some dental work done when I lived in Mexico City. It cost about one-third of what it would have cost in the United States. My *dentista* was an attractive young woman, twenty-eight years old, a graduate of the University of Mexico. She was gentle and polite and rather shy. She knew no English, so we spoke entirely in Spanish. From her I quickly learned the words for *drill, cavity, novocaine,* etc.

I looked forward to the appointments with my pretty *dentista*. She was very neat. Her hair was always brushed and perfectly in place. I remember her leaning over me, and the slight smell of perfume. It is not often that a young woman is so close to a man in a non-sexual way. It was definitely a sensual experience. As she leaned over me I could smell her, I could hear her quiet breathing, I could even feel her warmth.

Domingo

When I lived in the village I had a weekly ritual. I would take a break from my work on Sunday mornings and go to sit in the plaza. The parish church faced on the plaza, and I would sit on one of the benches and wait for the eleven o'clock mass to let out. A few minutes before noon the church bells would start to ring, the huge wooden doors would swing open, and the people would pour out and begin to cluster in front of the church. I would get up and walk over to mingle with them.

I remember the scene well: everyone dressed in their best clothes, all the generations mingling, everyone talking, the old people watching their grandchildren, formal intro-ductions and presentations on all sides, much laughter, the young people eyeing each other, the little girls with their hair brushed and shining.

It lasted for about ten minutes. I would move about, listening to the voices speaking Spanish, looking at the various people, just responding to it all. It always put me into a fine mood. Once I innocently asked a little boy why all this was happening. He looked at me and said, *"Porque es domingo."*

Drinking

Finding a decent place to drink can be a problem in many parts of Mexico. Except in tourist towns and large cities, a good bar does not usually exist. In many towns the only place available for drinking is an ordinary restaurant that stays open late. The students and young people in Mexico do not generally go to bars to drink. They will buy six-packs of beer and then go off in a car or to an apartment.

In many of the good bars in Mexico City, it is not the custom for women to be present, unless they are prostitutes. I did take women into a few of these bars, but only after checking out the place first and asking the bartender or owner if it was all right. Even if it was a respectable bar, there was a risk involved. And the woman had to understand that some of the men would assume she was a prostitute.

On many occasions I lamented the absence of a good bar. It is a pity that Mexico lags behind the United States in this important respect. There were times, especially in the tropical lowlands, when I would have given anything for a tall gin-and-tonic in an air-conditioned bar. There were other times when I had just met a young woman and we wanted to have a drink, but there was no place to go.

Eduardo

In Mexico City I was friendly with a twelve-year-old boy named Eduardo. He lived in the next building, and whenever he saw me on the street he would ask me to help him with his English. We would go up to his family's apartment, sit in the living room, and he would practice speaking English with me. I remember that he often confused *chicken* with *kitchen* and *hungry* with *angry*.

Eduardo and I enjoyed not only a rapport but a kind of equality. My superiority in age and experience was compensated for by his knowledge of the Spanish language and the social customs. And it was his country that we were in, whereas I was a foreigner. In these and other ways we had a mutually agreeable friendship.

Eduardo had a large family that included a beautiful fifteen-year-old sister, with an incomparable young body, and I would wait for her to appear. I often hinted to Eduardo that perhaps she would like to practice her English also. But Eduardo jealously guarded me and would not let any of his brothers and sisters come near us. I was *his* American friend.

Eduardo was shy and polite, and I liked him very much. Whenever I brought him children's books in English from the Benjamin Franklin Library, he would be very happy. Eduardo had eleven brothers and sisters, and once I made a list of the names and ages of all the children in the family. There was Maria Elena (23), Lourdes (22, married), Pilar (21, married), Cecelia (18), Antonio (17), Virginia (15), Eduardo (12), Gabriela (11), Guillermo (9), Guadalupe (8), Beatriz (4), and Elsa (5 months).

Education

I think the experience of living in a foreign country, especially an underdeveloped country, is an important part of one's education. I was twenty-four when I went to live in Mexico. It was the first time I had lived outside the United States. The time I spent there was a strong influence, but it was only years afterwards that I could begin to evaluate it. In many ways the experience was an antidote to some of the more offensive aspects of the American way of life. I see now that living in Mexico changed me and that I learned a great deal.

It was in Mexico that I stopped wearing a watch. One day I took it off and never put it on again. My concept of time had changed, and a watch had become unneccessary. From the

Mexicans I also learned not to rush. I learned how to sit quietly in a plaza and be content and do absolutely nothing. That was no small accomplishment for someone who grew up in a success-oriented suburb, devoted to producing contestants for the rat race.

I learned about poverty and minimal living in Mexico. It was an important part of my education, and it gave me a lasting distaste for bourgeois comforts. Anti-materialistic values and principles became much more meaningful. I observed how the Mexicans lived simply, how they survived on low incomes. After seeing that most Mexicans ate tortillas and beans three times a day, my own food requirements were considerably modified. It was all useful information, and it came in handy during the years of voluntary poverty back in the United States.

Eggs

Eggs are prepared in a number of ways in Mexico. I ate them almost every day, and to hell with the cholesterol count. *Huevos rancheros* were perhaps my favorites. These are fried eggs that are served on tortillas, with a mild-to-hot tomato sauce on top. The problem with *huevos rancheros* is that they can vary in different places from superb to terrible.

A more dependable dish was *huevos Mexicana*. It is standard in all parts of Mexico and is usually made well, mostly because it is so simple that it is almost impossible to ruin it. *Huevos Mexicana* are eggs scrambled with bits of onion, tomato, and chili pepper. You can ask for it without chili if you want.

I would often have *huevos Mexicana* during the evening, although some of the Mexicans thought this practice to be very curious. It is also a good dish to have as a last resort. If I asked what there was to eat in a small *lonchería,* and looked over at the stove, and if nothing looked or sounded good, then I might order *huevos Mexicana*. This dish is served with tortillas or rolls. If you ask for an order of beans on the side, it makes a nutritious and substantial meal.

Eggs are also scrambled with *chorizo,* the Spanish sausage. When this dish is made right, and the *chorizo* is of good quality, it is perhaps the best of all. In parts of northern Mexico, a favorite scrambled-egg dish is *huevos con machaca.* I never did find out what *machaca* is, but it appears to be some kind of dried meat.

Egrets

On my motorcycle trips through the tropical lowlands, I often saw cattle egrets and cattle together in the fields. It is an association that is very pleasing to view. The cattle egret has been described as "an old-world heron that has been undergoing a phenomenal extension of range." I also saw snowy egrets in various parts of Mexico. In my opinion the most attractive bird of this type is the common egret, also called the American egret. It is quite large, with black feet, a yellow bill, and immaculate white feathers. This graceful and beautiful bird is interesting to watch. It is a fine sight to see these birds flying up from the shallows or coming in for a landing. At times they seem to fly almost in slow motion.

El Metro

The new subway in Mexico City, called *El Metro* by the Mexicans, is a pleasure to ride. It is modern, quite inexpensive, and a welcome addition to the traffic-clogged city. The stations are clean and bright, the orange-painted cars roll smoothly and quietly on rubber tires. The system is French-designed and French-built, and riding *El Metro* gave me a new appreciation for French technology. The system is so quiet you can barely hear the trains coming into the stations. They *whirr* and sound more like sewing machines than trains.

If only the cars were air-conditioned, the system would be the best in the world. The arrangement of the rubber wheels is interesting. There is a second set, smaller and mounted horizontally, that rolls against vertical rails and provides lateral stability. *El Metro* may be of French origin, but it has now passed to the Mexicans, and the usual customs prevail. When a train opens its doors, the people on the platform do not wait for those exiting to get off. Instead, they shove forward, and there is an unneccessary crush.

I heard hilarious descriptions of white-clothed Indians from remote areas encountering *El Metro* for the first time. Each station has both a name and a pictorial symbol, for those who cannot read. They are still about one-fifth of the population of Mexico. Several easy-to-see strip maps are located in every car. While riding, it is fun to figure out the connection between the name of each station and its symbol.

It is a bit strange to be in the larger stations during rush hour, among the shops and fast-food stands, with hurrying crowds and popular music in the air. It is a preview of the future, of the new Mexico. *El Metro* works a curious effect upon the poor people of Mexico City, and somehow they look their best while riding on it. A pair of ragged children look much better sitting in a new *Metro* car than walking on the street.

Ensalada de Frutas

When I emerged from my hotel in the morning, one of the first things I did was to keep an eye out for the street vendors with carts who sold *ensalada de frutas*. It is available in most parts of Mexico, but in some towns and cities it is not sold at all. This delicious street-snack is made of fresh fruit that is cut into small pieces and mixed together. *Ensalada de frutas* is usually served in a paper cone, with a toothpick as the eating utensil. The vendors normally put salt, lime, and chili on it. but I held them off and just took a squeeze of lime.

The mixture of fruit may contain banana, papaya, watermelon, orange, cucumber, pineapple, honeydew, *jícama,* mango, strawberries, cantaloupe, and whatever else is available. *Ensalada de frutas* was one of my little pleasures in Mexico. I associate it with tropical towns and the beginning of the day. Many times I stood against a wall on a busy sidewalk, eating the freshly-cut fruit, enjoying the morning sunshine, and watching all the activity.

Erica and Winfriede

It is much more common for two girls to travel together in Mexico than for a girl to travel by herself. Therefore I usually met pairs of girls instead of just one. Instead of sitting in a plaza or under the *portales* with one girl, I was more often sitting with two. Such threesomes were the rule and not the exception. I will not go into the various aspects of this situation, and the little problems that it sometimes presents for a man.

In Mérida I met two girls from Germany named Erica and Winfriede. I met them in a small *restaurante* when they conveniently sat down at a nearby table. They were both from Munich and in their mid-twenties. We all did not care much for Mérida and the Yucatán, and thought that the region was overrated. But I enjoyed walking about Mérida and visiting the ruins with the two girls. I spent much time with them. They were very easy to be with, and I liked their company.

At that time it was late May, and the so-called rainy season had not yet started. It was very hot and humid in Mérida, even at night. Several times Erica said, "Ve are alvays

sveating here in dis terrible heat . . . ." I remember that I
would tantalize them with descriptions of the chilled German
wines they left behind. As a poet once wrote:

> German wines,
> the tapering bottles:
> Green from the
> Moselle Valley,
> Brown from the Rhine.

Erica and Winfriede were both robust young women.
They spoke English well enough, but used German with each
other when they wanted to communicate quickly. Several
times I knew they were talking about me, and it was a little
disconcerting. What the hell were they saying?

Erica wore a sexy outfit to explore the ruins at both Uxmal
and Chichén Itzá. It was a mini skirt combined with a tank
top that revealed two glorious patches of blonde armpit-hair.
The outfit drove the Mexicans wild. I told her about the
looks they gave her, but she didn't care, she just wanted to
keep cool. "I don't care how I am looking, I care how I am
feeling."

One night we had a fine time drinking rum and Cokes in
the patio of my hotel. It was an attractive patio, with
comfortable chairs, a large mango tree, and many plants and
flowers. We had it all to ourselves. Erica and Winfriede
brought a six-pack of Mexi-Cola, while I provided the rum.
At that time a half-liter of good Mexican rum cost about two
dollars. Winfriede became quite bombed. She even talked
about her sex life when she was a teenager in Munich. "You
are so American," she kept telling me.

Erica and Winfriede both had the marvelous attitude of
the German female towards sex, which might be summed up
as "Sure, why not?" But it was much too hot. Only a sex
fiend would have been interested. It was just as well, because I
could not decide whether I preferred Erica or Winfriede.
One was physically more attractive, the other had a more
appealing mind and personality.

Fiesta

The Mexicans are crazy with fireworks, and probably think that safety precautions are for sissies. I remember a 16th of September celebration, the equivalent of our 4th of July, in the town of San Miguel de Allende. I was caught in a surging crowd only ten feet away from giant fireworks displays; small boys were kicking a rocket cart around in the street; and the *rebozo* of a woman next to me caught on fire. The woman only laughed, and her companion patted out sparks in her hair as though it was great fun. I remember that they were using hot-air balloons as targets for the rockets, actually an ingenious idea. A rocket accidentally hit the police station, and then the spire of the cathedral.

Film

The cinematic counterpart of this book would be a highly personal, semi-documentary film that would run for two or three hours. In addition to all the incomparable things that film can do, it would contain hundreds of closeups of the faces of the Mexican people. On the soundtrack would be music, commentary, the sounds of Mexico, and a wide variety of voices speaking in Spanish. The film would greatly complement this book, which represents only a small part of my Mexican experience. The writing of it was saddening in one respect, because there was so much that I could not communicate with words. I especially regret that I could not communicate the smiles, the laughter, the expressions, the sounds of the voices, the little exchanges in Spanish. With film and the proper soundtrack, used together with this book, I could have far better communicated my Mexican experience.

Fish

Pescados ahumados are small fishes, usually caught that same morning, that have been smoked for a long time over low coals. Often they are prepared and served by the wife and children of the man who caught the fish. I had *pescados ahumados* at little beach-shacks in fishing villages on the west coast. The fish are very inexpensive. You point to the one you want and it is served to you immediately with limes and tortillas. They can be very tasty if they have not been cooked too long. With a bottle of cold beer, a *pescado ahumado* makes a nice lunch during an afternoon at the beach.

Flask

Those small flattened containers for carrying liquor go by several names, among them hip flask, pocket flask, and travel flask. Whatever the name, such a flask is almost essential equipment when traveling in Mexico. I owned one of good quality that I had purchased in San Francisco. It was used many times on my motorcycle trips, most often to contain rum and tequila from unfinished bottles. Then when I arrived at the next hotel after a long ride and began to unpack, I was all set for a relaxing drink afterwards. I did not have to go to a liquor store immediately in every town. The travel flask also came in handy whenever I happened to meet women at unexpected times. And I still remember the first time that I traveled on a Mexican train with a flask full of tequila. Ahead was a long and tiring ride, but that time I was prepared.

Frutería

In Mexico City I often patronized the *fruterías,* the shops that sell fresh-squeezed juices or *jugos* from tropical fruits, as well as the fruits themselves. They are located all over the city, but I most often went to the one in my neighborhood. It was an independent and old-fashioned *frutería,* not one of the modern chain-store operations. The owner was a man with a walrus moustache who apparently resisted change. He still preferred to make the standard *jugos* with a juicer and not the newer *licuados,* which are made with an electric blender.

I was a steady customer in this place, and the men who worked there always recognized me and said hello. There was a large selection of tropical fruits. Some of them had strange, voluptuous, unearthly shapes, as though they came from a Venusian jungle. Many were mediocre when eaten, but made a delicious juice. I usually tried a different one every time.

After I made my selection I would watch the man cut the fruit and toss it into the juicer. The fruit arrived almost daily from different parts of tropical Mexico, and I would often ask where it came from. In this *frutería* I eventually tasted the juice of the mango, papaya, sweet granadilla, star-apple, *jamoncillo,* guava, *membrillo,* purple granadilla, mamey, sapodilla, pitaya, *zapote,* cherimoya, and *guanábana.*

Girls

For an American with limited Spanish, it is probably easier to climb Mount Everest than to succeed with the typical Mexican girl. It can be done, for the attitudes are slowly changing, but you must be willing to expend much time and effort. Many men figure that it is simply not worth it. There are too many American, Canadian, and European girls who are traveling in Mexico.

With the Mexican girls it is frequently maddening, as they are so attractive. I loved to have little conversations with them and make them smile. Most of them are clean and neat, charming and polite. There is a softness and femininity about them, and also something about the voice quality that is very appealing. Guanajuato is perhaps the most painful place to be in this respect, for the town is filled with pretty university students.

When I lived in Mexico I could easily see why men wanted to marry such fine young women. Several times I wondered what it would be like to marry a doctor's daughter from a city like Morelia or Querétaro. I thought an intelligent young woman from Mexico would make a very good wife, especially if she spoke English and had been to a university and had also done some traveling abroad.

Goats

In most regions of Mexico, goats are an important part of the subsistence economy. Many times on my motorcycle trips I passed herds of goats by the roadside. They thrive on rocky, semi-arid terrain that is unsuitable for agriculture and will support no other type of livestock.

I rather like goats, especially the young ones. They are attractive little creatures, and much more intelligent than sheep or cattle. In addition, the economics of raising goats in Mexico appealed to me. All a man needed were two or three nanny goats, preferably pregnant, a billy goat, and a boy to watch over them in the fields.

This could be the beginning of several large herds of goats, producing quantities of milk, cheese, meat, and skins. It was all very profitable. The young goatherds would work for low wages, and the other expenses involved were minimal. It is surprising that Wall Street is unaware of the economics and profit potential of the goat business. I can almost imagine a boom, sometime in the future, in goat stocks.

Grievances, Irritations, and Dissents

The unplanned development and real-estate speculation that is happening to the best parts of the Pacific Coast . . . . The reactionary influence of the Catholic Church, which is still strong in Mexico . . . . Bullfights . . . . All the things that are unfixed and unrepaired, that are broken down and do not work . . . . The dullness of so many of the Mexican women. . . . The repressed sexuality. . . . The frequent lack of road signs. . . . The child labor . . . . Those of the *nouveau* middle class who are so fashion-minded and consume so frantically . . . . The second-class buses, especially in hot and humid cities like Mérida and Veracruz, that are packed with standing people . . . . The annoying stream of vendors, shoeshine boys, and beggars in some restaurants . . . . The sons-of-bitches who passed me on the road with only inches to spare . . . . The way they are destroying Chapultepec Park by using the land for various buildings . . . . The smog in Mexico City . . . . The make-believe elections with no real opposition to the PRI candidate . . . . The minimum-expense roads that are constructed without shoulders . . . . The rude way that some children and teenagers will laugh at foreigners right in their presence . . . . The gross lack of imagination in naming things: Parque Morelos, Avenida Juárez, etc. etc. etc. . . . . The way many Mexicans will not stop to help people who have been injured in auto accidents. . . . Some of the characters who work in the Pemex stations . . . . The Mexicans who callously exploit other Mexicans . . . . The way Mexican men, supposedly so polite and gracious, will bump into a girl on the street and not even apologize. . . . The cruelty towards animals. . . . The low doorways where I often bumped my head . . . . The tiny paper napkins in restaurants . . . . The clichés about Mexico that are put forth in tourist advertising . . . . The border towns . . . . The obscene contrasts between rich and poor . . . . The general unavailability and low quality of urban maps. . . . The tortoise-like service in some restaurants . . . . The motor vehicles with rusted-out and

47

missing mufflers . . . . The inefficient closing of most stores
and offices for two hours during the early afternoon . . . . The
fact that the hit-and-run driver seems to be the national
model . . . . The gross inequality between the sexes . . . . The
way many Mexicans seem unable to form lines and wait their
turn, and therefore think nothing of stepping ahead of you . . . .
The way they drive . . . . The way some streets change their
names every few blocks . . . . The confusing non-system of
street numbers that exists in many places . . . . The way a man
who collapses on a sidewalk will often lie for a long time
before someone stops to help him . . . . The callous disregard
of the motorist for the pedestrian. . . .

Guacamaya

The scarlet macaw is found in areas remote from man, in the
low-level jungles and rainforests of Tamaulipas, Veracruz,
Tabasco, Campeche, and Chiapas. The bird is quite large,
often measuring thirty-eight inches from beak to tail. It is
bright red, with a long red tail, and has wings of red, yellow,
and blue.

The plumage is far more brilliant than that of the other
macaw found in Mexico, the green or military macaw,
which is more common. The scarlet macaw is also larger.
Only the blue-and-yellow macaw, which is not native to
Mexico, rivals it for brilliance. I regret that I never saw this
grand bird in its native habitat. What a magnificent sight it
would be to see one in flight!

The Mexicans appreciate the beauty and noble qualities of
the scarlet macaw. It is frequently kept as a pet in Mexico,
where it is called a *guacamaya*. I saw a number of these birds in
shops, markets, and hotel patios. One time I stayed in a hotel
in San Miguel de Allende for over a week and came to know
a *guacamaya* rather well.

The hotel had a large and attractive patio that was filled
with plants, birds, and flowers. I passed the cage of the

guacamaya many times a day. He was a formidable creature, and we all respected his beak and kept our distance. I would often sit quietly in the patio when he was out of his cage and just watch him. As far as I could tell, the *guacamaya* never took his eye off me.

I quickly became an admirer of that bird. It was a pleasure just to look at him. His face alone was fascinating, and his feathers were exceptionally bright. I loved to watch him preen himself, especially when he would spread his great wings.

The *guacamaya* had a number of characteristics that appealed to me. He was as independent as a captive bird could be. He seemed to fear no one. He was intelligent. His life span was almost as long as that of a human being. He had pride and dignity. His appearance was nothing less than magnificent.

The way the *guacamaya* walked around the patio was very comical. The first time I saw it, I started laughing. The bird heard me and stopped walking; possibly he understood why I was laughing and was offended. I liked to read in that lovely patio, but was uneasy when the bird was out of his cage and walking around. He was like a snapping turtle with feathers, and I always felt that he was sneaking up on me. Fortunately his tailfeathers dragged on the patio floor and made a slight sound.

My motorcycle was parked in the patio, not far from his cage. One afternoon I watched the bird waddle over to it. Soon he was climbing up on the motorcycle, slowly swinging from part to part with his beak and claws. After that the bird did it every day. At the end he always perched on the handlebars.

The *guacamaya* was unable to talk, but he made a lot of noise. I could not pass his cage without feeding him something or he would make a great racket. I respected the bird, but never trusted him. The hotel maids had told me hair-raising stories of what he had done to people with his terrible beak. So when I fed him peanuts or raisins, I would place them on the end of a stick.

The *guacamaya* must have known that I was one of his fans. I was probably the first one to feed him cashew nuts. They were expensive enough so that I would not eat them myself, but I fed them to him. After I introduced the bird to cashew nuts, our relationship became more intense. Whenever he saw me enter the patio, he would let out a squawk of joy.

Guadalajara

Guadalajara was for me the terminus of the first part of a long trip, and it was also a refuge. I had driven on the motorcycle all the way from the Arizona border, most of it across harsh terrain on the dangerous west coast highway. It was late August when I arrived, up from the roasting-hot country below. Guadalajara meant a cool climate, and also civilization, for it was a real city. Later I was to realize that in Mexico I generally felt more at home in cities than in small towns and villages.

There are three cities in Mexico, all at elevations of approximately one mile, that share the reputation of having the best climate. They are Oaxaca, Cuernavaca, and Guadalajara. The fact that Guadalajara is also the second largest city in Mexico is misleading and means little. The capital is ten or twenty times as active and bustling. Guadalajara is to Mexico City roughly what Boston or Philadelphia is to New York.

I like Guadalajara very much. It is pleasant, and the pace is leisurely. There is a remarkable amount of open space, in the form of adjacent plazas, in the center of the city. It is a fine area for a walk in the early evening. The eastern end of the longest plaza is the best place to view the sky during a good sunset.

I was in Guadalajara another time during the week before Easter, which is called *Semana Santa*. I remember that I spent two hours on Thursday evening, leisurely walking around the plazas and nearby *portales*, mingling with all the people. It was a memorable experience. The crowd was mostly composed of family groups, and they were relaxed and happy. It was the first (and best) day of the long holiday.

I spent a number of mornings wandering around the Guadalajara market, which may be the outstanding attraction of the city. It is one of the largest, most colorful, best designed, and most interesting in Mexico. I especially like the design of the Guadalajara market; it is architecturally distinctive. Instead of *Mercado Libertad,* I wish it was named for the man who designed it. We who responded to the market are in his debt, and it would be nice to at least know his name.

In Guadalajara I liked to observe the activity on Sunday evenings in the *neverías* or ice-cream shops that are across from Parque Morelos. They all have jukeboxes and are filled with high-spirited young people, mostly teenagers, sitting at crowded tables and talking among themselves. The youth and energy of these young people is a fine thing to see. I suppose that Sunday evening in the *neverías* is one of the high points in their week.

Guadalupe and Asunción

When I lived in the village I studied Spanish at home for about an hour a day. But it was not enough to simply study Spanish, I also needed practice in speaking it. I found that the best way, and the most enjoyable, was to make friends with the various shopgirls of the village and have conversations in Spanish with them. I had already discovered that for some reason I understood women better than men.

Most of the shopgirls in the village were teenagers, but a few were in their early twenties. Some were very pretty, and they were all still single. The girls were always available and they had little else to do. They often would be leaning in the doorways of their shops, arms folded, looking slightly bored, watching the slow-paced activity of the village.

I often wondered what these girls thought about. My guess is movies, clothes, cosmetics, their *novios,* other young men, romantic daydreams, things to eat, the *serenata* on Sunday, their families and girlfriends, fiestas that were coming up. I remember that on Saturday they were often happy, probably because they were looking forward to Sunday, which is the big day in the Mexican week.

It was depressing to think of the cloistered lives ahead of these girls after marriage. They were all martyrs-to-be. Most of them would have children, begin to put on weight, and become restricted to their home and family. When I knew them, however, they were still slim and single.

I remember that I liked especially two attractive girls, bright-eyed and intelligent, who worked in the *librería* or bookstore after school. Their names were Guadalupe and Asunción, and they were seventeen and sixteen. They used the familiar form with me right from the beginning—it was so good to hear that *tú*—and we quickly became friends.

Guadalupe and Asunción always took the time to speak slowly and clearly for me, and corrected my Spanish whenever I made a mistake. They took pains to teach me the idiomatic expressions. Some people have a special skill in being able to converse with those who do not know their language well, and Guadalupe and Asunción both had it.

The friendship between the two girls was interesting to me. Asunción would call her friend either "Lupe", "Lupita", or "Lupitita", progressive diminutives, depending upon the context and how affectionate she felt. I observed a great deal of physical contact between them, and on the street they usually walked arm-in-arm. They often had their heads together in the *librería,* talking intimately about something. I was careful not to show a preference for either girl, although I had one.

Not many people in the village bought books, so Guadalupe and Asunción always had plenty of time for me. I spent many an afternoon talking with them, and it was great fun. I

remember that we always took turns buying the three bottles
of Mexican soda pop at the end. It was a ritual.

Guanajuato

The first time that I saw the town of Guanajuato, I was
amazed at its beauty. It immediately became one of my
favorite places. I think it should be declared a national
monument, like some other towns in Mexico. A walk in
Guanajuato at the right time, during the early morning or
late afternoon, can be a memorable experience: the low sun
on buildings, the narrow, climbing, twisting streets, the
lovely scenes and views, the little *plazuelas*.

Guanajuato is a town for architects and city planners to
visit. The way of life is so completely different from that of
an American suburb. People simply *walk* everywhere. I can
think of no town in Mexico where the private automobile
would more properly be banned.

An environment like Guanajuato is the way more people
ought to be able to live. There is a strong sense of community
there that I appreciated very much. The people seem to have
great pride in their little town. I think the beauty and
humanity of their environment works a marvelous effect
upon the people of Guanajuato.

Guaymas

Guaymas is a seeming contradiction in terms: a desert port. It
is situated on a bay where the desert meets the sea. Nowhere
in the United States does this unusual juxtaposition occur. I
had never seen such a thing, and it was one of the attractions
of Guaymas for me.

It is the arrival in Guaymas that is especially significant.

Most of us have come down from the north, across the Sonora desert. Approaching Guaymas we have the contrast of the harsh semi-desert and the blue Gulf of California. The cactus even grows right down to the beaches. I still have a color postcard of the Gulf of California as seen through cactus.

I enjoyed the life of the town very much, especially the area around the market. It is a lively place where all things are available. Some people feel that Guaymas is only a hot and dusty town, with too many tourists. I suppose this is partly true. The Gulf of California and the region surrounding it is increasingly becoming a vast recreational area for Americans. John Steinbeck in *Sea of Cortez* mentioned the tourists in Guaymas, and that was back in 1940.

Guaymas Bay has an unusual sight: cactus-covered little islands. The blue water in the Gulf of California is teeming with many species of fish. If you get a chance to go fishing or skindiving, by all means go. Guaymas is the center of a rather interesting area. Until a few years ago, there were jaguars in the nearby hills and canyons. About fifteen miles from Guaymas is what James Norman describes as "the great saguaro forest, a unique, brooding forest of cacti, a favorite breeding place of colorful parakeets."

Guidebooks

I have checked out all the guidebooks to Mexico and can recommend several of them. The first is *Terry's Guide to Mexico* by James Norman. At this time I think it is the best all-around guidebook to Mexico. There is a separate section about it elsewhere in this book. Also recommended is *The People's Guide to Mexico* by Carl Franz. It is published by John Muir Publications, a small press in New Mexico. The book may be hard to find, but it is worth the search. For the low-budget traveler it is almost a necessity. This book is filled with valuable information that can be obtained nowhere else.

The People's Guide is written with a good deal of charm and humor. I remember that in the index it says "Bordellos, see Whorehouses." The epigraph is a remark by a Texas border patrolman: "Boy, when you cross that Rio Grande, you in *another country!*" The tone and writing of *Terry's Guide* and *The People's Guide* are very different, and sometimes in hilarious contrast. I often found it amusing to go from one book to the other.

Both of these guidebooks are examples of how books are really a great bargain. Thousands of hours of legwork and research went into each one. They will save the traveler much time, trouble, and expense, and make his trip far more enjoyable. Yet they are available for only a small purchase price, and will then pay for themselves many times over.

Makens' Guide to Mexican Train Travel by James C. Makens is a slim paperback that is published by a small press in Texas. I found it useful. It is an oddly engaging book, mostly because it is so honest and unpretentious. If you have room, and are interested in the birds and animals of Mexico, also bring *A Field Guide to Mexican Birds* by Roger Tory Peterson and *Wildlife of Mexico* by A. Starker Leopold.

Héctor

One time I had a motorcycle breakdown in a small town in the middle of nowhere. I was on my way to the Yucatán and was a long way from a source of motorcycle parts. The Mexican mechanic that I found was a young man named Héctor. He was very friendly to me and missed dinner with the family of his *novia* in order to look at my bike.

I remember standing over his shoulder and watching him take my engine apart. He worked rapidly and skillfully, and I began to have confidence in him. Finally he said to my relief that the little bearings were causing the noise: the *chicos,* not the *grandes*. It turned out that the nearest bearings for my type of motorcycle were in Mexico City, 350 miles to the north, but this did not bother Héctor. He would simply use bearings for another type of vehicle. Like most Mexican mechanics he was skilled at adapting parts and improvising repairs.

Héctor began to speak casually of a grinding operation, of taking off a few thousandths here and a few thousandths there. He eventually decided to take 55/1000 off the connecting rod and put in oversize bearings. When he said that, I remember thinking: *I hope he knows what he is doing.* But it turned out to be all right, Héctor did a fine job. I eventually put another 7500 miles on the motorcycle and never had any more bearing trouble.

Because of that breakdown I was forced to remain in Héctor's town for an entire week. At the time I thought it was bad luck, but now I see it as very fortunate, a blessing in disguise. Because I had the time, I did many things that week that I would not normally have done.

Helmets

I never wore, or was forced to wear, a motorcycle helmet in Mexico. Some Mexican cities and states have helmet laws, but the police there seem to ignore the tourists. At any rate, I was never stopped. I hate motorcycle helmets with a passion. I think the helmet laws in the United States are an abomination and should be repealed or declared unconstitutional.

Motorcycle helmets have to be put on and taken off much too frequently. When you get off the bike, you have to carry the damn thing with you. They are extremely uncomfortable in hot and humid weather. They contribute to the irritability of the rider, which tends to take his mind off the road. They increase the chances of an accident by cutting down on awareness, visibility and especially hearing.

Motorcycle helmets give a false sense of security. They

protect only one part of a soft and vulnerable human body. They decrease the chances of a fractured skull, it is true, but increase the chances of a broken neck. Their added weight and wind resistance are considerable on a long day's drive, and increase fatigue. They cause the rider to turn his head less, which is one of the ways he spots a potentially dangerous situation.

From an aesthetic point of view, which is perhaps the most important one to me, motorcycle riding is an entirely different experience with a helmet. The openness, the unlimited visibility, the wind in your hair, the sense of freedom is gone. It becomes much less fun. It is almost like being inside, and the experience is ruined.

A large number of motorcycle riders will have serious accidents whether or not there are helmet laws. It makes me wince to see the speed at which foolish and reckless young men drive on busy streets, often much too close to the vehicle in front of them. This type of rider is headed for the hospital or graveyard, irrespective of any efforts to protect him. Because he pushes the accident statistics up, must other riders be forced to wear helmets?

Although a surprising number of men who are middle-aged or older ride motorcycles, they are mainly enjoyed by the young. I suspect that the repressive helmet laws are in a subtle way also anti-youth laws. Young people on motorcycles are disturbing, at least subconsciously, to many people. They represent a spirit of openness and freedom that is contrary to the prevailing ethic, to the usual middle-class values.

The helmet laws are enacted by state legislators who supposedly believe in a minimum of government regulation. But the laws are prime examples of Big Brotherism. There is a direct parallel with Prohibition. Why not a law forbidding boys from climbing trees, because they might fall out of them? Or a law making it a criminal offense not to wear rubbers when it rains?

The helmet laws have made me wonder about state

legislators, specifically about their ability to evaluate accident statistics. The laws are approved as wise and effective by millions of people, but most of them do not ride motorcycles. It is an example of one category of people telling another category what to do. I strongly feel that the choice of wearing a helmet should be left up to the individual. There are a number of good ways to cut down on the rate of motorcycle accidents, but the helmet laws are not one of them.

Highway

It is over a thousand miles from Nogales to Guadalajara on the Mexican highway designated as CN-15. I came to regard that west coast highway as a two-lane killer, somehow much worse than other highways in Mexico, and was glad to arrive in Guadalajara and be done with it. The motorist has to be constantly alert for a variety of hazards. These include tired drivers, slow trucks, and speeding buses. Much of the country is flat and uninteresting, almost hypnotic, and drivers tend to become bored, careless, mesmerized, and fatigued. The Mexicans often drive too fast, sometimes in unsafe vehicles. Sundays during the late afternoon on a hot day are the worst. The *machos* have been drinking and are frequently driving old cars filled with women and children. I saw one horrible accident near Culiacán in which seven people died.

Hotels Part I

During the year I lived in Mexico I took many trips on my motorcycle, to almost every part of the country. The total time of all my trips added up to over five months. During that time I must have stayed in at least sixty Mexican hotels. In every town there was always a hotel that was most suitable for me, and after a while I became quite skilled at finding it. I usually stayed at the unpretentious hotels patronized by families, Mexican students, and the Mexican traveling salesmen, the *viajeros*. These hotels were clean and inexpensive.

I always planned to arrive in a town early enough in the late afternoon so that attractive hotel rooms were still available. Finding a hotel was easier with the motorcycle than any other way. I was highly mobile, had excellent visibility, and parking was easy. In most towns I would just ride around until I spotted a suitable-looking hotel. I would begin by riding around the plaza and on the streets leading from it. One of my requirements was that the hotel be centrally located.

In my pocket while I rode the motorcycle were ripped-out pages from a guidebook that described inexpensive hotels. These pages were psychologically useful. They meant that I was coming into a strange town with something rather than nothing. But guidebook information about hotels is often outdated, and most of the time I found hotels on my own. I knew where to look and what to look for.

When I arrived in a town I always assumed there would be half an hour of looking before I found a suitable room. I often went to three or four hotels, sometimes more. It takes a lot of looking to find a good hotel room, but I figured it was worth the effort. An attractive room in every town made an enormous difference to my trips.

I soon learned that in Mexico the price of a hotel room has little relation to its attractiveness. It is true, the attractive rooms cost about the same as the dark and depressing rooms. I also learned that the appearance of a Mexican hotel from the outside means little. From the street it may be run-down and unpainted, it may even resemble an abandoned building. But inside there may be two tiers of spotless rooms, light and airy, set around a lush tropical courtyard.

59

I always stood across the street and just *looked* at the hotels before going inside. It only takes a few seconds, and that way I could count the floors, tell something about the layout, and figure out where the best rooms were likely to be. The desk clerks often hold back these rooms for repeat customers. This practice is perfectly reasonable: why should they give the best rooms to one-time-only American tourists?

Sometimes I would have to look at three rooms in a hotel before finding one that was satisfactory. It is a matter of wearing down the resistance of the desk clerk, and convincing him that you will not settle for less than the best he has to offer. I became rather skilled at this little game. It is almost fun when conducted with the elaborate Spanish manners.

I came to prefer the colonial-style hotels with several floors of rooms built around an interior court. But I was surprised to find that many of the newer hotels have rooms that are bright and attractive, and also reasonably priced. Some of the old hotels seem not to have been refurnished since the Mexican Revolution, and often have rooms that are dark and depressing. In general I preferred the newer or renovated hotels, with much better rooms at almost the same price.

Many of the Mexican hotels have interior rooms with no windows. I would never stay in such a room, only if I was desperate. It would be too much like being in a prison cell. But everyone has his own standards for hotels. I often met European and American students who stayed in even cheaper hotels than I did. Sometimes I felt guilty when I heard the prices they paid, and wondered if I was becoming bourgeois. I checked out some of these hotels, however, and found that they usually had interior rooms that were dark and depressing. I think these students went too far in their economical approach to travel. They made it an end in itself.

The first thing I always said to the desk clerk was *Buenas tardes*. Those two words always seemed to make a difference. Then we would talk about the room situation: the prices, how many were available, what floors they were on, whether or not there was a bath, and so on. Eventually I would be heading for the stairs with two or three keys in my hand. I cannot understand how some people will take a hotel room without looking at it first. It is even the custom in Mexico.

Occasionally I saw rooms that were ideal, but then discovered one important thing that was in disrepair and made the room unacceptable. It was always very irritating. Sometimes this happened in attractive hotels with good locations, at a time when I was tired from a long day's drive on the motorcycle. But I learned that everything must be tested: the lights, the ceiling fan, the lock on the door, etc. If I did not test all these things, I might be sorry later.

I only took rooms on the upper floors, with lots of light and air, where I could see the sky. If such a room was not available, I simply went elsewhere. Unless there was a fiesta or it was a tourist town in season, it was almost always a buyer's market for hotel rooms in Mexico. On the upper floors there is often a breeze, less street noise, and more privacy. I could walk around with the windows open and little or no clothing on. In hot climates I seldom wore any clothes in my hotel rooms. What was the point?

Sometimes in the tropics the rooms on the top floors of hotels become too hot, because of the sun beating down on the roofs. The ideal upper floor is therefore the second from the top. But I learned that in roasting-hot weather the afternoon sun on a wall can make even these rooms unbearably hot. I would then, like a cat, seek out a dark place, which usually meant a room on the ground floor.

The rooms that I chose on the upper floors, which was most of the time, often had views of the town. Sometimes I had two or even three windows. My preference was for a window that faced east, for then I could be awakened by the sunrise. It is very pleasant to have morning sunlight streaming in the open window of a hotel room. And I loved to get up at first light and be on the streets early in the morning. It is one of my favorite times in Mexico.

Hotels Part II

Once I found a suitable hotel room, it was only the beginning. The rooms in these inexpensive hotels are usually quite Spartan, and there was still work for me to do. Besides adapting to the idiosyncrasies of the hotel, I had to set the room up.

Among the petty irritations in these hotels are the frequent lack of such things as wastebaskets, sink stoppers, and *ganchos* or clothes hangers. When I would ask for *ganchos,* the desk clerks often said they would be brought to my room "in a little while," which can be a polite or evasive way of saying "No" or "Do not ask for things that you do not really need." Sometimes the *ganchos* arrived, but more often they did not. I was used to this kind of thing and cheerfully accepted it. It was just another example of what has been called the Mexican lie.

And so I acquired the habit of poking around vacant rooms on my floor and looking for things to bring back to my own room. I would creep from room to room, looking for items like *ganchos,* chairs, wastebaskets, and water pitchers. I did it often, and would think: The *Gancho* Thief strikes again! If I could not find a wastebasket, I would put a small bureau drawer on the floor and use it for that purpose. I never saw a stopper for the sink and had to carry my own with me.

Some of the hotels have hot water only in the morning, say from six to ten. That was no problem, I simply planned to take a shower during that time. Many of the inexpensive hotels in tropical climates provide no hot water at all. For some women, or a bearded man, or a man with an electric shaver, this is only a minor inconvenience. The water tanks are usually located on the roofs. By midday or early afternoon the sun has heated the water to lukewarm, and it is quite tolerable for a shower.

Mexico seems to be the land of the 25-watt bulb, and many of the inexpensive hotels have insufficient light for reading.

They also have few electrical outlets, which I needed for my immersion heater and electric shaver. I therefore had to carry a few items of electrical equipment wih me, so that I could provide outlets and rig up a reading light if it was necessary.

My equipment included a multiple outlet, an extension cord, two screw-in outlets, one push-pull socket with an extension cord, and a plug-in socket with multiple outlets. Naturally I wanted to wire these hotel rooms in the easiest and most efficient way, using the least equipment. It was sort of fun: every room was a new layout, a new situation, a new challenge. I used all these items, and weird combinations of them, at one time or another. If it was necessary I could wire a room for my use from a single overhead socket.

These reading lights that I rigged up, usually suspending them with cord above the head of the bed, were quite essential. I considered my hotel rooms to be also places to read and study. Sightseeing is much more enjoyable when it is broken up with reading and resting back in the hotel room.

On my trips in Mexico I did most of my reading and writing of letters in bed. It was the only way, for there were usually no desks in the hotel rooms I stayed in, and if there were, they were ridiculously small and uncomfortable. I was therefore propped up in bed, reading or writing, for several hours a day. I found that a clipboard was very handy for writing letters.

Hotels Part III

Occasionally I encountered an inexpensive hotel that was on the American Plan, an arrangement that I loathe. Unless a hotel is located in the middle of a wilderness, such a plan makes no sense to me. But usually, with a heart-to-heart and eyeball-to-eyeball talk with the owner or manager, I was able to negotiate my way out of this situation. I had an entire repertoire of reasons why I could not eat at the hotel. The

63

"special arrangement" that I obtained also got me the room at a much lower rate. I have always hated the American Plan with a passion. It gave me some satisfaction later to see my co-guests, the captive diners, shuffling into the hotel dining room, while I made my way out of the hotel and onto the streets, a free man.

After checking into a hotel, I would wheel my motorcycle inside and park it in the court or patio or lobby. The desk clerks thought nothing of this. Evidently it was common practice with motorcycles. They even seemed glad to have it in some hotels, especially since it was new, clean, and attractive. The parked motorcycle served as a conversation piece, and while passing through the lobbies I often saw men standing and talking about it. Because of the motorcycle I also enjoyed an instant rapport with the young sons of the owner, manager, or employees. The boys were usually intensely interested in the machine and asked me endless questions about it.

I never had any problems bringing a girl up to my hotel room, although I heard of men who did. The Mexicans can sometimes be very proper and puritanical about this, just as in some European countries. My technique was to use a combination of summoned-up charisma and overwhelming mental force, so that the desk clerk would never open his mouth. I would also psych up the girl before we entered the hotel. We would then bluff it through, acting as though everything was perfectly natural and respectable.

I went up on the roofs of these hotels whenever it was possible, for the views of the town, the surrounding mountains, and the sky and clouds. The morning was the best time. I was also able to observe the rich and varied roof-life below me: the *azoteas,* plants and flowers, caged birds and animals, women washing and hanging out clothes, and so on. Some of the hotels I stayed in had old-fashioned Spanish roofs, with red tiles set upon a wooden framework. I often looked at these roofs and admired their beauty and simplicity. Some were very old, with the rooftiles covered with moss.

64

My hotels were sometimes old and run down, but they were always spotlessly clean. I was impressed with the amount of labor that was expended every day in keeping them clean. Mostly it was done by girls and women. I saw them in the hallways and often had little exchanges and conversations with them. They usually smiled easily and were very friendly to me.

After I had been at a hotel for a while, it was sometimes not an easy matter to leave. I had to say good-bye to everyone, which took some time. In Mexico I had a number of memorable experiences as I was departing from hotels. There were numerous little conversations in Spanish, often as I was loading up the motorcycle. Many times I was touched to realize that someone who had been helpful and friendly to me was genuinely sorry that I was leaving. They often asked when I would come back, and I would say perhaps next year. It was so much easier to say that.

Hotels Part IV

My hotel in San Juan del Rio had a small menagerie of caged birds and animals in the courtyard. There were ducks, rabbits, geese, parrots, parakeets, guinea fowl, a fox, a badger, and a barn owl. In Guadalajara I had a garret-type room on the top floor with a window that overlooked the city. Another hotel in a tropical village had French doors and a balcony that opened onto palm trees and sunny tile rooftops. In Veracruz I had an upper-floor room in an inexpensive hotel that had a fine view of the harbor and the Gulf. In *The People's Guide to Mexico,* Carl Franz says, "We stayed in a hotel that featured a giant tortoise that roamed through the corridors all night, shuffling and scratching its claws against the tiled floor."

My hotel in Oaxaca had a wood-burning water heater in the bathroom. Twenty minutes before I wanted to take a shower, I would strike a match and light the fire. The inexpensive fuel used was sawdust and wood scraps, rolled up in a cylinder of old newspapers, with a bit of fuel oil added. This hotel had a lot of personality. In the courtyard was a lime tree next to a grapefruit tree next to a pomegranate tree, all with fruit. From the roof there was a splendid view of the rooftops of Oaxaca and the green hills and mountains surrounding it.

I ran into one hotel where the owner, a peso-pinching old woman, turned the electricity off during the day. I threw a fit when this happened the first time. But the old woman calmly told me that if I wanted to read, I could sit by the window and use natural light. I went unhappily back to my room . . . defeated by a little old woman. Afterwards I sat by the window and read by natural light.

One time I stayed in a villa-type hotel that had extensive grounds. There were a number of gardens, fruit trees of all kinds, and a wide assortment of birds and animals. Every day there was an uproar before dawn: parrots whistling, roosters crowing, pigs grunting, ducks quacking, burros braying, turkeys gobbling, macaws squawking. It seemed that only the cats were silent. This hotel was perhaps my favorite in all of Mexico. In the morning there was sunshine on the orange trees outside my window, and birds singing in the branches.

Hotels Part V

I shopped almost daily and kept small amounts of food in my hotel rooms. At one time or another I had dates, cheese, raisins, candy, *pepitas,* mangoes, peanuts, bananas, canned tuna, and sliced ham. In the markets I always kept an eye out for *plátanos pasados.* These are partially-dried bananas, brown in color, which are usually sold in plastic packages. They are very tasty and keep for a long time. A kilo on my hotel bureau would last me a week.

Occasionally the maids in the hotels would nibble at the food I had on the bureau. I once surprised a girl as she was eating some of my Sonora dates, and I thought she would have a heart attack. She gasped and almost choked on the dates. The girl thought I had left the hotel, but I had only been up on the roof. I was always happy to discover that some of the food was missing in one of my hotel rooms. It gave me pleasure to think of a maid secretly enjoying herself.

In one hotel there was a chubby teenage maid whom I suspected of having a sweet tooth. One day I put an assortment of foil-wrapped chocolates on the bureau and then counted them. It was like setting a trap. Sure enough, when I returned to my room, two of the chocolates were missing. I did it every day after that, setting my little trap for the chubby teenager. It was great fun. She never took more than two. When I departed from the hotel I left her a nice assortment of chocolates on the bureau.

Huaraches

There are different styles of *huaraches,* the Mexican sandals, in almost every region of Mexico. It seems that the higher the elevation, the heavier they are. At the time I lived in Mexico, the best *huaraches* for use back in the United States came from seacoast towns like Mazatlán and Acapulco. The *huaraches* made there were thin-soled, light-weight, and very comfortable.

But it is not so easy for many American men to buy *huaraches*. The Mexicans have smaller feet, and it is difficult to find the larger sizes, so usually you must have them made to order. I remember the workshop in Mazatlán where I had my *huaraches* made. There was an old man, who was the owner, and two young men, who were his sons.

On two pieces of paper I made penciled outlines of my feet. I gave them to one of the sons and watched him begin to work. He worked rapidly and skillfully, and it was a pleasure to watch him. I always love to observe a skilled craftsman. The radio was playing popular music all the time. There was much laughing and joking among the old man and his two sons and the people who came into the workshop.

I was glad that I was able to watch the making of the *huaraches* from beginning to end. After I tried them out— they squeak when they are new—and paid for them, I had a little talk with the old man. Among other things we discussed the prices of cowhides.

Hummingbirds

One time in the Jalisco countryside I was almost mesmerized by a flowering tree that was buzzing with scores of hummingbirds. I remember that they were gloriously iridescent in the bright sunshine. These pugnacious little birds are most common in tropical latitudes. Fifty or sixty species are found in Mexico alone. The Mexicans like to have the little birds around and often put out red feeders for them. A Mexican woman once told me, stating it as fact, that hummingbirds are attracted by the color red.

Images

Mechanics working on a broken-down bus . . . . The pat-pat-pat sound of tortillas being made . . . . The calendars hanging on the walls of Mexican cafes . . . . The sad-faced shopkeepers . . . . Fat priests and skinny children . . . . The sound of a Mexican band in the distance . . . . The plaza in Veracruz at sunrise . . . . The flamboyant signatures of officials . . . . Bird cages and potted flowers everywhere . . . . The sound of churchbells . . . . The beautiful light-green stone used for buildings in Oaxaca . . . . Small children streaming out of a school . . . . The clop–clop–clop sound of the hooves of burros on cobbled streets . . . . The sight of palm fronds waving in the breeze against a blue sky . . . . The parades of schoolchildren on fiesta days . . . . A pet ocelot walking about a house furnished in Mexican colonial . . . . The smell of the exhausts of ancient buses . . . . Babies peeking out from the depths of *rebozos* . . . . Pretty girls walking beside their formidable mothers . . . . The streetcar in Veracruz that runs to the beach . . . . Guadalajara on Sunday morning. . . .

Immersion Heater

Whenever I traveled in Mexico I carried a few items with me for making hot beverages in my hotel rooms. I had an immersion heater, plastic mug, spoon, instant coffee, bouillon cubes, and tea. The immersion heater was the ingenious little device that made these comforts possible, and I recommend it to all travelers.

But in some cities in Mexico there are voltage surges that will burn out a small appliance. It took me a while to find this out. In Guadalajara I burned out three immersion heaters on three mornings in a row, and didn't know why. It was driving me nuts, because I didn't know the reason. When the third one burned out I almost had a cardiac arrest.

Then a hotel maid told me that the current in Guadalajara was *muy fuerte*. And later an electrician in an appliance-repair shop explained it to me in a more scientific manner, and even drew a little graph. So for the remainder of my stay in Guadalajara I drank instant coffee made from water at room temperature. It tasted terrible, but I thought it was better than no coffee at all.

Invisible

When I lived in the village I liked to walk around the market at night. In the darkness they could not see that I was an American, and I could observe undetected. I would often buy a *taco de carnita* at a curbside stand and then go sit in a doorway to eat. My clothing was dark and inconspicuous. I would blend into the shadows. After I finished my taco I would sit and watch the passing people. There was usually much activity, for they would be setting up for the next day. I would be completely unnoticed. No one expected to see an American sitting in a doorway.

Jeanne and Maria

One night I was in my room in a run-down hotel in Tepic, reading on my bed. It was late and very quiet, but I kept hearing a weird kind of English being spoken somewhere. The voices were both female. I could not concentrate on my book, so I stepped outside my room, listened carefully, and eventually traced the voices to one of the other rooms.

I stood in front of the door for a few seconds. Then I summoned my courage, figured what the hell, and knocked on the door, rather loudly for some reason. The voices immediately stopped. Later they told me they were terrified, and thought it was the secret police.

In this way I met two outstanding young women: Jeanne, who was French, and Maria, who was Portuguese. We had a great talk that night for over three hours in their hotel room. Jeanne and Maria were a unique pair, and I liked them very much. I soon went back to my room and brought the remainder of a bottle of tequila that I had. We sat on the bed and drank tequila and talked until long after midnight.

Jeanne and Maria were both in their early thirties. They had been backpacking for several months in the mountains

70

near Tepic, gathering information about the Indians in the area. Tepic was their base and they returned every few weeks. They worked as a team: Jeanne was a journalist and Maria a photographer. Because there were no roads, only trails for horses, they took short flights from the Tepic Airport to remote villages and started to walk from there. Maria told me that on their last trip they had to go two weeks without baths.

Jeanne and Maria were very close friends and I was touched to see it. When one was sick or injured, the other took care of her. They both were widely traveled and had numerous skills and interests. Jeanne had interviewed many well-known people for French newspapers and magazines. Maria was not at all a typical Portuguese woman: she had been trained as an engineer, was an amateur pilot, had worked in France for a computer company, had even rebuilt a Volkswagen engine. Like many Europeans they were both fluent in four or five languages. "Why do you speak English together instead of Spanish?" I asked. "Because English is much faster," said Jeanne.

Jukebox Cafe

Every small town in Mexico seems to have its jukebox cafe where the teenagers hang out. Only middle-class kids are usually there, the poorer ones cannot afford it. I often sought these places out in my travels, for I liked the feeling of them. They are crowded and at their best after school is out and during the early evening. In general the Mexican teenagers are very attractive young people. They have the same exuberance of their American counterparts, but appear to be neater, cleaner, and better-mannered.

The high spirits in these places when they are crowded are almost contagious. The kids sit at tables, talking among themselves, and the jukebox is always playing. Usually there is a mixture of Mexican and American popular songs. The whole scene is marvelous fun to observe: youth, energy, and spirit in abundance. I would have a cappuccino or a bottle of Mexican soda pop and just take it all in. It always put me into a good mood.

Kirsten

In an insect-ridden hotel in Palenque I had the good luck to meet a lovely young girl from Norway. Her name was Kirsten and she had a room two doors away from mine. She was only nineteen, but had been traveling on her own or with a girlfriend since she was sixteen, mostly in France and southern Europe. Kirsten and I visited the ruins together and soon became very friendly.

She was a real traveler and could travel for months with just her Norwegian-made backpack. When she told me it was highly organized, I mentioned that I would be interested in seeing everything she had with her. To my surprise Kirsten immediately agreed to show it all, and for the next twenty minutes we went over everything in her pack, wallet, and pockets. It was hilarious for both of us: rapid questions and answers, and many laughs. I remember that she blushed when she came to a few items.

La Roqueta

Most beaches face out to sea, where there is nothing to look at except the surf and sky. But La Roqueta at Acapulco is on an island and faces the bay, part of the city, and the surrounding hills. I remember how enjoyable it was to sit on the beach and look across the water at the fine panorama. During the afternoon the clouds build up over the foothills of the Sierras, and if conditions are right it can be a magnificent display. One time I counted seven cumulonimbus thunderheads, with anvil-shaped tops. I remember that the sun was striking them in a beautiful way. These towering clouds, which contain immense amounts of energy, sometimes reach as high as 45,000 feet.

Life in the Village

Shopping every day in the market . . . . The friendly exchanges with the tradespeople . . . . The walks to the *banco* with the little piece of paper from the United States . . . . Random encounters with friends around the plaza and other places . . . . Lunch in the sunny patio . . . .The bright sun in the blue sky . . . . Looking down from the balcony of the *casa* at the varied activity in the street . . . . The ritual of reading the newspaper with *café con leche* in the cafe on the plaza . . . . The pace is delightfully slow . . . . Everyone has plenty of time for leisurely conversation . . . . Walking to the *tortillería* for hot tortillas . . . . The dry semi-desert air . . . . Listening to the transoceanic radio of a friend . . . . No one has a telephone . . . . No one has urgent appointments . . . . The evening walks through the quiet streets . . . . The Mexican band that plays on Sunday evenings in the plaza . . . . The twenty-year-old American movies in the one moviehouse . . . . Reading at night in the quiet *casa* . . . . The brightness of the stars in clear air at 7000 feet . . . . Sitting and looking into the low fire before bed . . . . Sleeping an average of eight hours during the cool nights . . . .

Loncherías

Guidebooks are highly unreliable and almost worthless for finding restaurants in Mexico. Much of the information is already out-of-date before the books are even printed, and afterwards the guidebook publicity is often detrimental. One of the best ways to find a place to eat in Mexico is simply to walk around and look for one. I usually explored the streets within two or three blocks of the plaza, or in some other area, and then choose the place that looked the best.

I came to favor the small *loncherías* with only a few tables, especially the ones that served a *comida*. These places were unpretentious and gave excellent value. A good *lonchería* (they are also called *comedores* and *restaurantes*) was often just a storefront with a small sign. After a few months in Mexico I was able to size them up in a matter of seconds. The best indication of all was a very ordinary-looking place, usually with metal tables and chairs, that was filled with people.

I sometimes looked at the menu in a *lonchería*, if there was one, but generally I ignored it. It is risky and unwise to order from a menu in such informal places. I learned that the best way was to look at what the other customers were eating, to look at the big pots and kettles on the stove, and most important of all, to simply ask what there was to eat. I would ask *"¿Qué hay?"* or *"¿Qué hay de comer?"* which means "What is there to eat?" It is a valuable phrase for the traveler in Mexico.

Because of idiomatic Spanish and regional names for dishes, there was often a short conversation about the ingredients. There was no other way. I seldom asked if they had a specific dish, for the answer would invariably be yes, and soon a small boy would be slipping out the door with money in his hand, off to do some quick shopping. And of course I would have to wait. The cooking areas in these *loncherías*, by the way, are often in easy view. Many times I ordered something and then was able to observe how it was prepared.

74

Loncherías are sometimes owned and run by one family. I was always a bit touched to see an entire family working together, and the ones I observed working in *loncherías* seemed to be harmonious. The mother usually does the cooking, the grandmother helps in the kitchen, the small children run errands, the father takes cash and oversees the whole operation, the son buses the tables, and the teenage daughter is the cute young waitress.

I was always pleased with myself when I found a good *lonchería,* and would go back again and again. Whole families eat in these places. It is a common sight to see a table of seven or more people, including a baby and a grandmother. Often there is no real door to a *lonchería,* and almost the entire front is open to the sidewalk. During the intervals between courses it is a diversion to look out at the passing people.

Lowest Moment

My lowest moment in Mexico probably occurred in Mérida, on a hot and humid day during the evening rush hour. In Mérida, because of the climate, the evening rush hour is even worse than in Mexico City, if such a thing is possible. I had not received a registered package containing three weeks of forwarded mail, and was hoping to get to the post office before it closed. The next day was some kind of fiesta and it would not be open. I was walking along a crowded, traffic-filled street, with a great deal of heat, noise, fumes and congestion. I was in a hurry, and drenched with sweat, but blocking the narrow sidewalk in front of me were a number of Maya women and children, walking slowly on little short legs.

Although it is humorous to think of this "lowest moment" now, at the time it was not funny at all. The package of mail was long overdue and contained money, in the form of American Express money orders, as well as important letters.

As I walked I was hot, tired, angry, and frustrated. Not only was I extremely upset, but I was not thinking or functioning well. All I could do was blame the people, and over and over again I muttered evil things about Mexico to myself. The most frequent mutterings I had were about the incompetence of the Mexicans, the screwed-up ways they did things, and how the country was run by idiots.

Machete

One of the secrets of traveling on a motorcycle is to take frequent breaks. After an hour or so under the hot Mexican sun, it is a great pleasure. I would often sit in the shade outside a little *tienda* or store and drink a cold bottle of Mexican soda pop. An incident once occurred in a small village near Tehuantepec, when I was taking just such a break on a motorcycle trip. There was a sullen-eyed man with a machete who stopped walking in the street and just glared at me. He had probably just come in from the fields, for he was hot and dirty. I was sitting in the shade, a few feet from my parked motorcycle, drinking a bottle of that Mexican soda pop called *Chaparritas*. The man just stood there for a long time and glared at me. I still remember his sweating face. Sometimes I think of him, the man with the machete, when I read about United States imperialism in Latin America.

Machismo

No book on Mexico would be complete without some mention of *machismo*. The subject is practically unavoidable. There are few women who hate *machismo* more than I do. It is nothing less than a mass sickness that affects a majority of Mexican men. On the road is where I hated *machismo* the most, and several times it almost killed me. I often wished that I could confront those men face-to-face and tell them what I thought of their mental state and their driving. There are other reasons than *machismo* for the Mexicans being such poor drivers, but I tend to blame it the most.

Magazine Stands Part I

The book-buying statistics for Mexico are said to be among the lowest in the world, as hardcover books are generally for the élite. But an enormous variety of newspapers, magazines, comic books, photo-novellas, and pulp novels are purchased and read. I spent a lot of time at the magazine stands in various places in Mexico. My favorites were on the busy streetcorners of Mexico City, where every square inch of space is used for the colorful display. It is hard to believe: there are thousands of publications, of every conceivable size and description.

It is very educational to spend time at these magazine stands, which tell a great deal about the Mexican people and their culture and society. One thing I noticed was that comic books and photo-novellas featuring various superheroes were very popular with boys and young men. For the girls and women there were the usual romances and love stories. The magazine stands, along with the moviehouses, are evidently an important source of supply for the rich fantasy-lives of most Mexicans. The quantity and frequency of this escape reading is what is significant and also a little disturbing. I often saw people who worked in busy and active places bury their noses in a comic book or photo-novella whenever they had a spare minute.

Magazine Stands Part II

At the time I lived in Mexico, *Excelsior* was considered by many to be the best newspaper. It was centrist and occasionally criticized the government . . . . *El Día* was a leftist newspaper. It often used a kind of revolutionary rhetoric that I found amusing, for example, "The gangster governor of Morelos" . . . . The fashion magazine *Claudia* once proclaimed *"La Revolución Sexual"* in Mexico. The article probably had little basis in fact, but would make eager reading for frustrated females . . . . *Claudia* delighted in using *Americanismos* such as super, bye-bye, O.K., sexy, pick-up (truck), bar, and garage . . . . A Mexican baseball magazine was called *"Pley Bol!"* One cover showed a star player hitting a *jomrón* . . . . There are classic comics in Spanish, sex and girlie magazines of all kinds . . . . I remember the fine covers by Carreño for the leftist magazine *¡Siempre!* . . . . One of the most popular comic books was *Kaliman, el hombre increíble.* I saw so many people reading it that I even bought a copy myself. But I learned that *Kaliman* was a sloppy and inconsistent composite of about ten different kinds of superheroes . . . . There is a magazine for women athletes . . . . I have seen an entire magazine stand broken down at night and methodically packed into a three-wheeled motorscooter cart. Early the next morning the man would presumably set it up again . . . .

Manga

I was caught in the rain many times on my motorcycle trips, sometimes in the middle of nowhere. Unfortunately I did not have the kind of foul-weather gear that is specially designed for motorcyclists to give complete protection against rain. The best is made in England, so I have been told. A heavy rain in the tropics has to be experienced to be believed. When I was caught in such a downpour, and no shelter was available, I got completely soaked. The only consolation was that it was usually a warm rain.

In a drizzle or light rain, however, I was all right, for I had a *manga de hule* that I had bought in the market in Puebla. A *manga* is a Mexican-type rubberized poncho with no hood. It is used by *campesinos,* bicycle riders, and men on horseback all over the country. If a passing driver saw me, he might have thought I was miserable, but I was relatively content. The *manga* broke the wind and kept me dry, and I was in an envelope of warmth under my jacket and sweater.

When it was not raining, the *manga* was rolled up and carried on the back of the motorcycle. It was also useful for walking around a town in the rain. Unlike carrying an umbrella, my arms were free. The *manga* was loose and comfortable. There was no hood to annoy me every time I turned my head, and to limit my vision and hearing. Walking in the rain in a Mexican town was great fun. Only my head got wet, which is really no problem in a warm climate.

Mangoes

The mango has probably been cultivated by man for over 4000 years. It is a fruit of great importance in many parts of the world and even has religious significance. It has a rich history and is mentioned often in ancient literature. The mango could easily be the national fruit of Mexico. An illustration of a mango tree, or a detail of the fruit with leaves, would be very suitable for one of the Mexican currencies.

I often watched street vendors with carts prepare ready-to-eat mangoes for sale to pedestrians. The most common method is to force the mango upon a sharpened stick, peel it, and then cut slashes in it. It is then a mango-on-a-stick. Almost all the Mexicans have chili powder sprinkled upon their mangoes, but I thought this practice was depraved. In Acapulco and some parts of Chiapas, the mangoes are nicely sliced and sold in paper cups or little plastic bags.

Slices of green mangoes are commonly taken with *mezcal* or tequila. The fruit also makes a delicious ice cream, and I once watched an *helado* man in his shop as he combined cream, sugar, and mashed-up mangoes to make mango ice cream. Many times I bought mangoes in the market or from the carts of street vendors and then brought them back to my hotel rooms. They are slurpy and hard to hold, however, and therefore not easy to eat. My technique was to sit on the bed and use a knife, an old newspaper, and a towel.

Unfortunately there are mangoes and there are mangoes. The ones I had back in the United States, usually from Florida or Hawaii and rather expensive, were attractive in appearance but mediocre in taste. In Mexico the quality varies widely throughout the country and depends upon many factors. The best ones I ever tasted came from the Veracruz area.

The Manila mango was introduced in Mexico in 1770 and is considered to be one of the finest varieties. In the state of Veracruz the growing conditions are ideal and a superb fruit is produced. I was once in Veracruz during mid-May, when the Manila mangoes are in season. They are sold everywhere from overflowing carts at very low prices. I bought a kilo every day and devoured them back in my hotel room. They were fabulous, and for a few days I went mango-crazy.

A full-grown mango tree at its peak, just when the first fruit is ready to be picked, is a magnificent sight. The trees often reach immense size, and a trunk twenty-five feet in circumference has been recorded. It is an attractive tree, thick and dark green. It also makes an excellent shade tree.

Several hotels that I stayed in had mango trees in the patios and courtyards. Birds often build nests in these trees. In one hotel I could step out of my room on the second floor and be on the same level as the branches and fruit. There were mornings when I stepped out of my room and just stood at the railing for a long time, responding to the sunlight on the green leaves, and looking up at the blue sky.

Margaritas

At twenty-four I was not used to drinking liquor straight. In addition I thought the taste of tequila was terrible. I drank tequila straight only under social pressure or when nothing else was available. In Mexico, especially when traveling, there was often no ice, nothing to mix liquor with, and sometimes even no glasses. Out of necessity we often drank tequila right from the bottle.

Seen from this perspective, the margarita, when properly made and chilled, is a great way to drink tequila. An old Mexican hand once told me that most Americans do not know how to use the salt on the rim of the glass. He told me that it should be taken into the mouth and then sucked for a few seconds before sipping the drink. This will serve to bring out saliva, he said, which helps to protect against the burning of the liquor. If made properly, the margarita is a rather harsh drink.

Everyone has heard of the margarita, but the tequila sour and the tequila fizz are smoother, just as Mexican, and taste even better to many people. The names tequila sour and tequila fizz are both partly *Americanismos*. To a Mexican bartender the second words are pronounced "sow-ear" and "feez." These cocktails, along with the daiquiri, are often made superbly in Mexico, because it is the custom in many places to use fresh-squeezed lime juice.

Mariscos

In many parts of Mexico, but especially on the west coast, I always kept an eye out for the sign *Mariscos*. The word means shellfish in particular but also seafood by extension. The Gulf of California, a fascinating body of water, teems with marine life and provides a rich bounty for the states of Sonora and Sinaloa. Within that region the seafood is almost always fresh and not frozen. I had delicious *mariscos* in numerous places between Guaymas and Mazatlán. Every morning the day's catch is iced and trucked to towns along the west coast highway from fishing villages such as Altata, Huatabampo, and Topolobampo.

The best time to sample these freshly-caught *mariscos* is shortly before noontime, before the real heat of the day, and also before the Mexicans get to them. *Mariscos* are sold from carts, at sidewalk stands, at market stalls, and in little restaurants. At the very least, from a small operator with a cart, there will be a pile of shrimp on a block of ice. Sometimes at a sidewalk stand there will be a long block of ice, with piles of clams, squid, conch, and shrimp. Many of the vendors make piles that are very neat and symmetrical, and it always delighted me to see them.

The simplicity of eating these delicious *mariscos* appealed to me, for all that was provided were cut-up limes and a hot sauce. In a few minutes I was finished and on my way, smacking my lips. Some of the market stalls and little restaurants also provided a *sopa de mariscos* or seafood soup, which was usually delicious. I was always asking *"¿Hay una sopa de mariscos?"* Along with the usual supply of tortillas, it made a filling meal.

Market

I always checked out the market in every town that I visited in Mexico. The market was so filled with sights that I only went there when I was alert and my energy was high, so that I could fully respond to it. It was one of my great pleasures to walk around at a leisurely pace and observe the age-old scene. The late morning is the best time to visit, when the people are fresh, not in the late afternoon or evening. The streets in the immediate vicinity of the market are also a good place to walk, for there is much to see there as well.

In the market in Culiacán I observed a scene that apparently takes place every morning. A number of men carry sides of beef from a truck to the butcher stalls inside the market. I was amazed at the sight: each man carries an entire side of beef by himself, on his back. The smaller men stagger under the bloody, hard-to-handle weight, which I was told is between 150 and 175 kilos. Anyone who thinks the Mexicans do not work hard should observe this unforgettable scene.

In the market in Oaxaca I watched a butcher, using a razor-sharp knife, cut up an entire pig with great speed and skill. I was impressed by his ability and watched until he was finished. Another time in Veracruz I watched an impassive-faced woman take a chicken from a cage and immediately kill it by breaking its neck. I was stunned, I watched with horror. It is such a commonplace act, yet at twenty-four I had never seen such a thing in the United States. I even dreamed about it that night: the squawk of the chicken, the sound of the neck breaking!

I walked slowly in the markets and stopped often. I always kept an eye out for a good place to sit down and watch the activity. There is so much to see: the faces of the people, the piles of strange fruits and vegetables, the pretty young girls behind the counters. In the market in Guadalajara I turned a corner and suddenly saw the most beautiful girl in the world. She was weighing vegetables on a scale.

In these markets in Mexico I remember the bustle and

activity, the smoke from all the *carbón* fires, the murmur of Spanish and Indian dialects, the mixed smells of many kinds, the popular music from many radios. The chubby-armed Mexican women would bump into me in the crowded aisles, their bodies soft but sturdy. I observed hundreds of them as they did their daily shopping. Mostly I remember the aprons, the black braids, the faded cotton dresses, the patient long-suffering faces.

Market Cafes

The longer I lived in Mexico, the less expensive the eating places that I patronized. It was a gradual process, with part of the reason being my increasing knowledge of Spanish and the Mexican customs. At first I ate in the American-style restaurants; then in the medium-priced Mexican restaurants that served a *comida;* and eventually in the small *loncherías* and at sidewalk stands and in the little cafes in the markets.

There was always a section of the market set aside for these little cafes, which are also called *fondas*. Since they were all together, there was an incredible mixture of food smells from the dozens of pots and skillets and cauldrons. The market cafes had either a counter or a long table or sometimes two or three tables. I usually preferred to sit at the counters.

There was never a menu, and the names of the dishes tended to vary in every region. I would sometimes ask the Señora, usually a chubby-armed woman with an apron, if I could look into the pots and see what looked best. Many times, before actually taking a seat, I walked down the line of cafes, peering at the stoves to see what looked good. Another way was to see what people were eating; then when something looked good, I would stop and order the same. In this way I discovered some unusual and tasty dishes. The whole idea is to see something first and avoid the handicaps of regional names and idiomatic Spanish.

I did not care if the people at the cafes looked at me as I peered at the stoves. They look at Americans no matter what they do. Many of the Mexicans seemed to be gratified to see an American eating in the market just like themselves. I was usually treated very well, and sometimes with special consideration. The women who ran the cafes were often strong and assertive, and many times I had the feeling that they were the heads of their families. I was impressed by the way some of them carried themselves with great dignity. They generally called me *joven*, which in my case meant young man.

The most interesting area of market cafes is in the town of Navojoa in the state of Sonora. The area is like a large patio, adjoining the market and open on one side to the street. There are two large trees and the tables are set out beneath them. Parts of the area of cafes in the Guadalajara market are also open and airy, but unfortunately the aggressive hawking there makes it less pleasant. Sometimes there are many cafes and it is difficult to choose. I would often go by a general feeling about the place, with an important indication being the faces of the people who were working there.

The market cafes sometimes have names. Often they are diminutives such as "The Little Badger." In the Oaxaca market is a cafe named *"La Abuelita,"* which means "The Little Grandmother." I was there once on a rainy night when two people were working, the delightful combination of a pretty teenager and her grandmother.

Market Sights

A woman with a small pig under her arm, talking with a friend . . . . A *campesino* selecting a new machete from a box of twenty-four . . . . Primitive scales: two pans, string, a stick to balance them, a rock that weighs one kilo . . . . A little girl in a tattered dress, sitting in a doorway with a lamb . . . . Different types of tropical fruit cut open so the insides can be seen . . . . When one type is cut in half, there is the pattern of a star . . . . A cafe owner buying two liters of raw milk from a vendor and then putting it on the stove to boil . . . . A burro loaded with two baskets filled with purple avocados . . . . An Indian woman spinning coarse yarn from raw wool . . . . A pen with day-old yellow ducklings . . . . Two old men playing Mexican checkers with bottle-caps as the pieces . . . . A boy carrying the dressed head of a bull on his own head . . . . Baskets of angelfish . . . . A man with a dozen birdcages tied to his back . . . . A small girl carrying a full-grown turkey in her arms and talking fondly to it: *"Pavito, pavito . . . ."*

Meat

Because of the high-carbohydrate diet that prevails in Mexico, I sometimes had strong cravings for protein, especially meat. In restaurants there were usually several types of beefsteak or *bistec*. This is the inexpensive Mexican "steak" that is fried and served everywhere. It is at its best when grilled over charcoal and then called *carne asada* or *carne asada al carbón*. This steak is thin and tough, but tasty with a good *ranchero* or *Veracruzano* sauce.

Rotisserie chickens are available in most towns in Mexico. When I had cravings for protein I would sometimes buy a small one, take it back to my hotel room, and eat the whole thing. It is not easy to eat a rotisserie chicken while sitting on a bed in a hotel room. My technique was to use an old newspaper and a towel, and then tear the chicken apart with my bare hands.

Some large markets have entire sections devoted to *birria* stands. *Birria* is barbecued goat, although sometimes they sneak in a lamb. I avoided these stands at first, perhaps because *birria* was too strange and foreign, because I didn't like the name, and also because there was a distinctive smell to that part of the market. But one time in Guadalajara I was in an adventurous mood and decided to try it. I found that it was very tasty, and had it many times after that. *Birria* is commonly served in a bowl, with lots of juice, and the usual tortillas on the side. With a bottle of cold beer or a *refresco*, it makes a nutritious and inexpensive meal.

Sometimes I would see a woman in the market selling *barbacoa* for tacos. *Barbacoa* is barbecued lamb or mutton, but sometimes beef. Instead of making tacos, I would order a quarter-kilo of lean meat, have it put in a bowl with some juice, and then eat it with a couple of tortillas. When *barbacoa* is made right, it is delicious.

Another way to satisfy the craving for meat was to find a *carnitas* stand. This is roast pork, and one of the favorite meats of the Mexicans. They usually make tacos from it. The Mexicans seemed to expect a mixture of meat and fat from the vendor, but I always asked for *pura carne* and got it—a quarter-kilo of nothing but lean roast pork. *Carnitas* are delicious, but would be even better with a good Texas-style barbecue sauce.

Meeting People

I thought it was relatively easy to meet other Americans in Mexico. People were much more free and open, and many of the restraints and social inhibitions seemed to be left behind at the border. I noticed that Americans in Mexico who were complete strangers often said "Hi" when they passed each other on the street. Partly it was psychological support in a strange and alien culture.

The smaller the place, the easier it was to meet other Americans. It was probably the most difficult in Mexico City. (I keep saying Americans, but I mean to include Canadians and most Europeans who speak English. In general, English-speaking people of non-Hispanic origin.

The vast majority are Americans, however, so I will use that word for convenience). I met these people in hotels, in restaurants, on the street, in the market, at the post office, under the *portales,* at ruins, in museums, at the long-distance telephone booths, in the plazas, at taco stands, on buses and trains, and in various other ways.

To an American man, there is nothing quite like receiving a direct look from a pretty American girl when in a foreign country. I thought it was absurdly easy to meet American girls in Mexico. There are so many possible openers. A common and unimaginative one that always works is "Are you Americans?" followed by a legitimate question about hotels or restaurants or anything else. I never attempted to meet girls at night in Mexico; in my experience that should always be done during the day.

It is not difficult to meet likely-looking American or European girls at the cafes under the *portales*. This happens most frequently in the tourist towns. I would usually sit down at an adjoining table, order something to drink, and eventually strike up a conversation. Naturally it would be easier if there was some favorable eye-contact first.

Mexican Day

The Mexican day has four distinct parts. First there is the extended morning, which lasts until the early afternoon, when the stores close. The morning is a good time to take walks, to do errands, to go to the market. It is an active time in Mexico. It is relatively cool, and there is shade until almost midday.

The Mexican afternoon begins when the stores close, a variable time but usually about one or two o'clock. I soon learned that it was a good time to get off the streets. There is some shade by mid-afternoon, but it is hot shade as opposed to the cool shade of morning. During the afternoons in

Mexico I would sometimes visit with friends; I might go to a restaurant for the *comida corrida;* if I was traveling and near the water, I would sometimes go to the beach; or I might go back to the *casa* or apartment or hotel room and nap or read or write letters. It was definitely no time to be on the hot, barren, and uninteresting streets. This afternoon period or *siesta* time is fairly long. It is the quiet part of the Mexican day.

After the morning, my favorite time for walks in Mexico was the early evening. The best part begins about thirty minutes before sunset, but this can vary because of surrounding mountains. Because of the effect of the light, a poet once called this special time of day The Magic Hour. The sky is just beginning to darken, and it is a time when earthly places are almost transformed. I think anyone who chooses to be indoors at this time is sadly lacking in sensitivity. It is one of the finest times to take a walk in Mexico. The heat of the day is past, the streets are filled with people, there is lots of activity and much to see.

It sounds moralistic and old-fashioned, but *early to bed and early to rise* is really the best way in most parts of Mexico. Except in resorts and tourist towns, there is simply not very much to do at night. The streets are usually deserted and uninteresting within an hour after the stores close. Nights in Mexico are best spent in the *casa* or apartment or hotel room, reading or writing letters or being with friends.

Mexicans

I soon learned that the word *Mexicans* is in some ways almost a meaningless word. The country is really a federation of diverse peoples, and it is better to call them *Oaxacaños, Chiapanecos, Yucatecos, Capitaleños,* etc. In general I liked the people of the highlands better than the people of the coastal areas. They tended to be more open and friendlier. Of all the regions of Mexico, I liked the people of Oaxaca the best, and found that they had a good reputation throughout the country. I also liked the northerners, who are closer to the ways of the United States. And the *Capitaleños,* because people in big cities are the same in many ways the world over.

It takes quite a while for a newly-arrived American to learn about Mexico and the Mexicans. For me there was a period of confusion and cultural shock before I adjusted to the Mexican ways of doing things. I soon learned about their elaborate rituals, about their seeming inability to say "No" or "I don't know." I found out that the *sub-gerente* of a Mexican bank will assure you that a check takes two weeks to clear, when it actually takes six. I learned to accept anything that was offered to me, even if I did not really want it.

Contrary to all the stories, I never had to bribe a Mexican official. They were consistently helpful and courteous. I remember one encounter in a government office, where I was getting nowhere against an incredible bureaucracy. I finally found a Mexican official who seemed interested in helping me out. The man listened patiently to my Spanish as I made my explanations. Then he nodded his head, picked up the telephone, and with a few words cut through all the red tape.

When I took my motorcycle trips throughout the country, the Mexicans that I encountered were almost always helpful and friendly. I was often moved by their little kindnesses. Several times in strange cities, men who had given me directions came after me, sometimes walking a half-block or more, to amend or correct what they had said. Many of the people went out of their way to be friendly. *Rancheros* treated me to beers, ice-cream vendors gave me free *helados,* shopgirls bought me Cokes.

The Mexican people are very polite, but I found it an advantage, and almost a weapon, to be even more polite than they were. For example I said *por favor* and *gracias* at every opportunity, sometimes too often. And I frequently used an introductory *buenos días* or *buenas tardes* before asking for something. These and other polite expressions, especially when used by an American, are very much appreciated by the Mexican people. It makes an enormous difference in the way one is treated.

I learned to be almost indifferent to the answers when I asked questions in Mexico. There seems to be no such thing as a cold fact, or an absolute truth, or irrefutable logic. I would often ask the same question three Mexicans and get three different answers. Perhaps they were all right, in their own way. The shrug of the shoulders, the helpless expression, the *¿Quién sabe?* That is what I came to believe in.

The Mexican men often scowl and look fierce with their big moustaches, but inside most of them are like baby rabbits. I found that the best attitude was to be open and friendly towards the Mexicans, courteous and very polite, but most important of all, non-threatening in any way. It is the various defensive attitudes of the Mexican that can cause ill will. If you give him nothing to be defensive about, then these attitudes disappear and he usually comes across as a very fine person.

Most of the girls and young women in Mexico are unfortunately too shy to speak what English they know. But many of the men have more courage and are eager to practice. I often had hilarious conversations with men where each of us clung with determination to the other's language.

Contrary to expectations, I never had trouble with the Mexican policemen. I often asked them for directions or information, and without exception they were courteous and helpful. One time a shopkeeper was rude and nasty to me for no reason whatsoever. Then a few minutes later I was given directions by a cop who was so friendly that he walked me part of the way there. Another time I talked with a policeman at an intersection, a gracious and polite man, who also gave me directions. Then he stopped the traffic so I could cross the street.

I sometimes parked the motorcycle by the side of the road

in rural areas to make a minor adjustment. Whenever I did so, a *campesino* would invariably appear out of nowhere. He would pass by, always at a distance and never too close. Nothing would usually be said, but it was clear that if I needed assistance I had only to ask. In towns, whenever I had to lift the motorcycle up the steps of a hotel, passing men were always very willing to help. Sometimes they were even dressed in business suits.

One time the *maestro* of a *taller mecánico* sweated for twenty minutes to loosen three screws on my motorcycle, the screws that hold on the generator cover. They had been over-tightened by another mechanic. The *maestro* was helped by two boys, assistants who were mostly sent to fetch tools. When he was finished and had loosened the screws, he refused any kind of payment. All I could do was buy him *una cerveza*.

I was often impressed by the honesty of so many of the Mexican faces. Not a single item was stolen from me during the year I lived in Mexico. A number of times I purposely left various objects behind me in my hotel rooms when I checked out, things I no longer needed. I was often touched when a maid would come hurrying up to me, usually as I was loading the motorcycle in front of the hotel, with the object in her hand.

The Mexicans must be among the most generous and considerate hosts on earth. It is a privilege and a compliment for an American to be invited into the house of a Mexican. It did not happen to me often. I noticed how they like to have birds around, how they fill their houses with plants and flowers. There is probably a psychological term describing a love for birds, but I do not know it. Whatever it is, the Mexicans have it in abundance.

Mexico City Part I

Mexico City is one of the most interesting and stimulating cities in the world, but it is also one of the most chaotic and confusing. The tourist without a knowledge of Spanish will have many difficulties. There are many little tricks to just getting around the city, but even if you know them, it is simply not possible at times to get from one place to another. The evening rush hour is one of the worst in the world. At other times it seems to be a continuous rush hour.

Many Americans are disappointed with Mexico City. They arrive, spend a few days, then leave earlier than they had planned. You really have to live there, as in any world capital, to appreciate Mexico City and fully respond to it. The tourist with only a few days is at a great disadvantage. He does not know the city, which is quite complicated in many ways. Transportation alone can be maddening. He often tries to see too much, and exhausts himself at the high altitude.

One cannot spend too much time sightseeing. Three or four hours a day is more than enough. It is much better to live in a great city and see it leisurely, in bits and pieces. It is all a matter of fatigue and attention-span.

There are so many Europeans in Mexico City, and it is so influenced by other cultures, that it is almost an international city. Parts of the downtown area have the rapid pace that is found in all the great cities of the world. One of the most attractive parts of downtown Mexico City is centered around Avenida Madero, between San Juan de Letrán and the Zócalo. It is very civilized and very European. Avenida Madero itself is worth examining, with its attractive paving-stones and nice little gutters. These are several pedestrian malls in the area, and the streets are exceptionally clean.

Mexico City now has almost as many fountains as Rome. They are delightful additions to the city, pleasing the senses of sight, sound, and smell. Several of the fountains are in the Alameda in the downtown area. The Alameda is without question one of the finest public parks in the world.

Mexico City Part II

When I lived in Mexico City I had a special sitting-spot by one of the fountains in the Alameda. I would plan to arrive there during the early evening, just as the sunset was beginning. At this fountain there were people to watch, it was the end of the day, I could hear the soothing sound of falling water. It was wonderful, and some of my finest moments were spent by this fountain. I often wondered why such a choice sitting-spot was not in great demand.

Mexico City is a good place for random walks, and I had my favorite streets with busy sidewalks and much to see. Many times I was in moods of intense joy and happiness, partly because I was twenty-four at the time and had all the leisure time I wanted. I must have spent hundreds of hours walking about Mexico City. Often I had a marvelous time but spent only a few pesos for buses, snacks, and coffee. One thing I remember is the unusual combination of a crisp September-morning feeling with a special spring-like smell in the air. There are many explanations for the distinctive smell in Mexico City. Some say it is from the thousands of *carbón* fires, and also from the pines of the surrounding mountains.

During these random walks I would stop whenever I saw a crowd gathered. It usually meant a pair of musicians or a street entertainer or a talented pitchman of some kind. At times there are heavy concentrations of these diversions. Once on the Avenida San Juan de Letrán it took me half an hour to walk four blocks.

The world's largest roller coaster is now located in Mexico City. For some reason it is called the *montaña rusa* or Russian mountain. It is in New Chapultepec Park, and when I was there on a Sunday afternoon I rode it in a car full of shrieking teenagers. The ride is a good one and will be enjoyed by all *aficionados* of roller coasters. The structure is new and presumably safe, but nevertheless I kept thinking, "I must be crazy, riding a Mexican roller coaster."

In Mexico City I appreciated seeing the children everywhere. It is an important dimension that is missing in most American cities. Colonia Polanco has many Mexicans of German extraction, and I saw many blonde-haired children there. It was always a surprise to hear them speaking Spanish. When I walked in Colonia Polanco I always tried to pick out the ex-Nazis. It is not difficult to imagine the older men in Nazi uniforms, with lügers.

There is endless stimulation in Mexico City, there is so much to see. I could not take a five-minute walk without being provoked by something. I never knew what I was going to see next. One time I was ten seconds out of my hotel on Calle Bolivar, when suddenly I saw a luscious teenage girl walking towards me, with a baby coati-mundi on her shoulder. I did not know what to look at, the girl or the coati-mundi.

Miscellaneous

In Mexico City I once took a walk in the *colonia* described by Oscar Lewis in *The Children of Sanchez*. I saw The Street of the Bakers, The Street of the Barbers, The Street of the Tinsmiths, etc. . . . . *Negritos:* dark cigarettes, very mild, with molasses in the paper . . . . In Tabasco I once saw an old locomotive puffing through the jungle, the steam blowing back the trackside vegetation . . . . A man told me that his wife had given birth to eleven *hombres*. Six had died, but five had survived to adulthood. Of the five, two were doctors and one was an architect . . . . Second-class bus: the buzzer is not working, so the driver has improvised by attaching a baby rattle to the cord . . . . Recipe excerpt: "Soak beans overnight, after washing them and picking out the pebbles" . . . . There are over 112 species of oaks in Mexico, and over 39 species of pines . . . . Once at a gas station in Chiapas, I threw an empty oil can into a trash barrel. Immediately five or six Indians ran for it . . . . Mexico City: the public writers under the *portales* in Plaza Santo Domingo, each one with a typewriter and a chair for the customer . . . . Approximately 70 per cent of Mexico is considered temperate and supports temperate types of vegetation and fauna. Only 30 per cent is considered tropical or frost-free . . . . The streets in Mexico City with concentrations of shops that specialize in certain items: I thought of them as The Street of the Electric Blenders, The Street of the Lampshades, The Street of the Guns, etc. . . . . A bottle of water-purification tablets is a necessity in Mexico . . . . I liked the tiny banks in rural areas with only one teller . . . . Once I stayed in a hotel room that had yellow walls, a pink chair, a green bed, and a blue bureau . . . . More than 650 species of fish have been identified in the Gulf of California . . . . In special areas on the outskirts of cities, usually called *La Zona,* are the *cantinas de mujeres.* Some of them are Federal whorehouses and are even patrolled by soldiers . . . . The Acapulco market has stalls of live iguanas . . . . Lázaro Cárdenas was an outstanding President of Mexico, from 1934 to 1940. The date that he expropriated the foreign-owned oil holdings is like a holiday, a source of national pride . . . . Calzada Independencia in Guadalajara, the part near the market, is very lively and a good place to walk at night . . . . The keel-billed toucan is another magnificent bird that is found in Mexico. It has roughly the same range as the scarlet macaw . . . . The hilarious way the Mexicans pronounce American brand names such as Texaco and Chevrolet and Quaker State . . . . In 1924 D. H. Lawrence moved to Mexico and lived there for a year. Of all the possible locations, it is significant that he chose Oaxaca . . . . I liked to imagine the nature paths in a Mexican National Rainforest . . . . To approximate miles from kilometers, multiply by six and drop the last figure . . . . Mesquite is used for firewood in many parts of Mexico. It is hard, heavy, and delightfully aromatic . . . . The best short story I read about Mexico is "The Man Who Looked Like Jesus" by Howard Fast . . . . Before the name of the new President is officially made known to the public, he is sometimes called *"el tapado,"* which roughly means "the corked one" .... Guadalajara to Nogales is a long but interesting train ride .... The great Alexander von Humboldt once spent a year in Mexico .... I sometimes saw Chicanos who were visiting the old country. They were often in big cars or station wagons, with Texas or California plates, and looked sleeker and more prosperous than the Mexicans.... Hot chocolate is a specialty in Mexico and can be delicious. Sometimes there are several types to choose from, such as *Española, Mexicana, Francesa,* etc. .... I remember walking on a hot night in a town in the Yucatán, and seeing many hammocks through the open doors and windows .... The puma or mountain lion has a remarkably wide range in Mexico. It is found throughout the country, in the mountains, the desert, and even the jungle .... The strawberry *paletas* or popsicles are bright red in color, often contain whole strawberries, and are usually delicious .... I once observed a simple funeral along the roadside in Guerrero. In front of a group of *campesinos* the body was borne shoulder-high on a rigid stretcher. It was covered with a sheet, and the brown feet were sticking out and shaking as the men walked .... "Of the seven species of cats found in North America," says the zoologist A. Starker Leopold, "all but the Canada lynx occur in Mexico." I wonder what would happen if a few pairs of the lynx were released in Mexico, perhaps on the slopes of the highest volcanoes .... Good dessert: Kahlúa on vanilla ice cream with flakes of shaved chocolate .... I appreciated the barnyard sights that are so common in Mexico and now so rare in the United States .... In the Acapulco market I once saw a woman roasting a large iguana on a spit. It was also the first time I had seen anyone basting a lizard .... A large saguaro cactus weighs ten to fifteen tons, is ninety-eight per cent water, may be over fifty feet high, and lives to be 200 years old .... I often carried a roll of those peppermints called *Menta Inglesa.* They helped to counteract the chili and spices in Mexican cooking .... In regards to bus accidents, Stanton Delaplane once said: "You go off the road in pine trees, and wind up at the bottom in bananas" . . . . Venison stew is common in the Yucatán, and quite inexpensive . . . . I once knew someone who had broken his arm and was taken to an English-speaking doctor. The doctor looked at his arm and said, "Terrible! Terrible! Terrible! But ees not too bad" . . . . Thirteen of the fifteen species of American rattlesnakes are found in Mexico . . . A man I met from Arizona could not remember the word *chicleros,* for the men who tap trees for chicle in the jungle. So he said, "Them chiclet fellers" . . . . The bright-colored tropical birds that live around the limestone wells or *cenotes* in the Yucatán . . . . Mexicana once had a flight from Mexico City to Mérida that touched down at Veracruz, Villahermosa, Ciudad del Carmen, and Campeche. On a clear day it provided magnificent views of the Gulf coast and nearby mountains . . . .

Molly

I remember a night in Mexico City when I met a Canadian girl in a seafood restaurant. For some reason it was a more expensive restaurant than the type I usually went to. The girl and I were seated at tables on opposite sides of a large room. We were the only English-speaking people, everyone else was Mexican. There were several families and a number of couples, all very subdued. No music was playing and the restaurant was very quiet.

First the girl and I exchanged looks and smiles. I saw that she was very pretty. After a few minutes I summoned my courage, figured what the hell, and got up and walked over to her table. There were about thirty people in the room, including the waiters, and by now they all had their eyes on me. If I was going to be put down, it would be embarrassing. Women should really be more appreciative of the things men have to do in order to meet them.

But it was all right. She was friendly and glad to meet

someone who spoke English. I asked her if she would like to share a table, and she said she would. Mine was in a better location, so we began to move all her things over to it.

Meanwhile I realized that all the Mexicans in the restaurant were observing us, evidently with some fascination. They had probably stopped eating so they could listen to every word. What a show we were putting on for them! I wondered afterwards what they thought, and what comments they made to one another. The middle-class Mexicans are usually restrained and very proper when they are in such restaurants.

I soon learned that my new friend was named Molly and that she was a social worker in Toronto. She was cheerful and intelligent. I liked her very much, and we had a good time that night. A few days later she had to fly back to Toronto and I saw her off at the airport in Mexico City.

Moments

Walking on the *malecón* in Veracruz during the sunset and early evening: warm air, nice breeze, harbor smells, red sky . . . . A wizened old woman in a market cafe, probably a great-grandmother with a lifelong mother-urge, cackling to me about my sunburn . . . . The open door to my room in a one-story hotel in a tropical village: the faces of three piglets, clustered together in the doorway, as they look at me reading on the bed . . . . Many times I would be passing through an obscure village, expecting to see nothing, when suddenly I would come upon a remarkably beautiful child or teenager . . . . Sitting on the motorcycle as it is parked beside a sugar cane field near Cuautla: a thunderstorm has just passed, clearing the air, and I can see snow-capped Popocatépetl, about thirty miles away, as clearly as it can be seen . . . . Swimming and sunning at numerous beaches on the west coast, from Guaymas all the way down to Salina Cruz . . . . On my way to catch the bus to Uxmal, I passed through the plaza in Mérida at 7:15 in the morning. It was beautiful: activity, cool air, long shadows, children walking to school . . . . A large herd of goats, with many kids bleating, filling a narrow village street: they separate to go around me and my stopped motorcycle, and then come together again behind me . . . . Topolobampo: a dignified-looking man is cleaning fish, rapidly and skillfully, with a razor-sharp knife. A pelican waits a few feet away. The man is very impressive for some reason, and I watch him for a long time . . . . Sitting in a sunny garden in Cuernavaca, looking up from flowers to palm trees to blue sky . . . . I still remember the blank face and resigned expression of a prostitute in a *cantina*. She was only a teenager and rather pretty. She was leading a middle-aged man through the door that led to the little rooms in the back . . . . On the fully-loaded motorcycle, surrounded by iguana-sellers in Guerrero: they are showing me all the different ways I can carry an iguana on the motorcycle . . . . The great joy I would feel while unpacking in a good hotel room I had found, in a town that was yet to be explored . . . . In the market a man sells me 100 grams of Sonora dates. I notice that he has the face and bearing of a prime minister . . . . Walking in perfect solitude along various beaches during the time before sunset . . . . The sole question from a Mexican border official: "No gons?" . . . . When it is crowded in *loncherías,* tables are often shared. One time in Morelia I was joined at my table by six bright-eyed girls who had just come from their *colegio* . . . . Walking past open doorways and looking into quiet patios: plants, sunshine, birds singing . . . . Near the beach in Playa Azul I came upon a baby asleep in a hammock. It was an appealing sight, I stood and looked at it for a long time. The hammock was the normal size, and in the middle, sagging close to the ground, was the tiny bundle . . . . In a market, a girl shows me the game she often plays with her pet coati-mundi: the girl tries to touch the little snout before it is tucked under the coati-mundi's foreleg . . . . Walking about the promenade areas of tropical ports on Sunday evenings, in

Guaymas, Mazatlán, Veracruz, Campeche, and Acapulco, listening to the music and responding to the young people.... Free tacos being passed out in a *cantina:* the face I made when I bit into one filled with dried blood .... Watching the desert sunrise from an open window as the train approaches Nuevo Laredo .... The middle-aged man who went into the back room of the post office in Mérida and diligently searched until he found my precious package, containing three weeks of forwarded mail. I will never forget the sight of him emerging with that package .... The *malecón* in Acapulco: watching pelicans diving head-first into the water .... One time, before buying a ticket, I doubted the effectiveness of the air-conditioning in a moviehouse in Veracruz. With a smile and a wave of his hand, the ticket-taker graciously bid me go inside and see for myself how cool it was, without paying first .... Walking before breakfast on a jungle path, green and lush .... The looks and smiles I would provoke from the women when I stopped to watch the operation of a *tortillería* .... In a cafe, the kindly *camionero* or bus driver who drew me an elaborate map of a route over unpaved roads .... I remember an early language-thrill with my new Spanish. It was on the first morning in Mexico, in the town of Magdalena in northern Sonora. I was able to ask my way to the bank, and then what time it opened .... In the little town of Huichápan, a pretty señorita showing me how her pet *ovejito* or lamb is trained to butt one's palm .... The child-in-arms in a crowded market who reached out and touched me .... Riding the motorcycle at low speed on the cliffside road above the ocean in Mazatlán: good views, seabirds above, bright sun, blue sky, the sparkling sea .... Early evening in Querétaro: a procession of children, all of them singing and carrying lighted candles, coming out of a small church. Although I am anti-religious, I am touched by the sight and have to watch .... Sitting in the shade on the steps of the post office in Acapulco, eating a sliced mango from a paper cup, watching the morning activity .... A little girl in a plaza who sells me a roll of peppermints: she puts her basket down, trusting me, and runs for change . . . . The open-window train for Mexico City slowly pulling out of Mérida at sunset . . . . The beginning of a *gran baile* or big dance on a Sunday evening in a town on the west coast: I stand outside with the others and watch the girls, bright-eyed and excited, as they arrive in pairs and groups . . . . Several men in a *lonchería* are watching soccer on TV when a funeral procession begins to pass by outside. One of the men quickly turns the sound off, but not the picture . . . . On the second-class bus to Tlacolula, responding to the exquisite beauty of a girl about eight years old sitting in front of me. I observe her hair, skin, lips, eyes, teeth, and ears. I listen to her melodic voice as she talks with her mother . . . . Watching TV from the street in Cuernavaca, standing in a diverse group of Mexicans: *campesinos,* shoe-shine boys, a businessman, two shopgirls. It is a comedy, and at one point we all break into hilarious laughter . . . . Mazatlán on a Sunday evening: sitting quietly on a bench in the plaza, across from the lighted cathedral . . . . Late one night in Guanajuato, as I was walking back to my hotel through the deserted streets, thinking about the mummies I had seen that afternoon: a burro snorted in a dark alley and scared the wits out of me . . . .

Monte Albán

I always walked slowly around the various Mexican ruins that I visited. I would sit down often in the shade and look about. Ruins are a good place to just sit and think. I contemplated the valuable perspective that a person gains from visiting ruins. One thing I thought about was the insignificance of so-called "success" back in the United States.

I remember one time when I was at Monte Albán, which is situated on a hilltop above Oaxaca. Aldous Huxley visited Monte Albán in the early thirties. In *Beyond the Mexique Bay* he describes the site as ". . . incomparably magnificent. Imagine a great isolated hill at the junction of three broad valleys; an island rising nearly a thousand feet from the green sea of fertility beneath it."

The books say that Monte Albán was once the center of several important cultures, among them the Mixtec and Zapotec civilizations that flourished long before the time of Cortez. It was a hot day when I was there. I remember that I was sitting in the shade at the eastern edge of the ruins, looking out at the magnificent view. The panorama included much of the enormous valley of Oaxaca, and extended all the way to the town of Zaachila, many miles to the southwest.

I had read that during the Pleistocene era, when there was more rainfall and the climate was different, the valley of Oaxaca contained an immense and shallow lake. From where I was sitting I could easily imagine that great lake . . . perhaps with a group of mammoths feeding at the edge. It was quiet that day and I could hear guitars from a hacienda far below. The Sierra Madre del Sur, green and cloud-tipped, was in the distance. I remember that I saw a tiny DC-3, glinting in the sunlight, as it took off from the Oaxaca airport. It was probably the daily flight to Mexico City.

I often thought about that view afterwards: the view from Monte Albán. I had already walked around the ruins that day. After the initial exploration, which will take from one to three hours, the ruins do not hold sustained interest for one who is not an archaeologist. The sun is hot and the tourists do not stay very long. I mainly appreciated the act of visiting the ruins. Mostly I remember the hot sun, the buzzing of the flies, the fallen building-stones lying in tall grass.

Moon

I remember a fine walk that I had one night on the outskirts of a village on the west coast. The sandy road I was walking on and the tall palms along it were illuminated by a full moon. It was a very quiet night. If I listened carefully I could hear the distant sound of the breakers. The little houses along the sandy road were lighted from within and sometimes I could hear low voices. The air was warm and tropical, and I could smell the fragrance of night-blooming flowers. After a while I found a low wall to sit on. I sat there for a long time, just listening to the sounds and smelling the air and looking up at the full moon above the palm trees. I remember that I was happy and content and completely at peace with myself. I see now that this was one of my finest hours in Mexico.

Motorcycle

I cannot imagine living and traveling in Mexico without the motorcycle. It made an enormous difference for me, and one of the reasons I liked the country so much was that I saw it in one of the best possible ways. Next to walking or bicycling, a motorcycle is the best way to see anything.

I had unrestricted vision on the motorcycle. There was no windshield on it, and I did not have to wear a hated helmet. By turning my head from side to side, I could enjoy a 270° panorama. I could look up and see the entire sky, which can be magnificent in open country.

I had no desire whatsoever to "make good time" on my trips, and would stop whenever I saw something interesting. Many times, whenever I came to a particularly lovely spot, I would stop the motorcycle by the side of the road, turn off the ignition, and just sit there in the silence and *look*.

The motorcycle meant increased contact with the Mexican people, and in this respect it was a valuable asset.

When I stopped somewhere, the Mexicans were usually very interested in the machine. It was better designed and more attractive than their own motorcycles. They would often stand around, discuss it among themselves, and ask me questions about it. In the many isolated places where I stopped, the motorcycle was a small event for them. It was something new and stimulating in another long and tedious day.

When I passed through a town for the second time, I often went back to the same hotel. If they remembered me, it was probably because of the motorcycle. When I pulled into a place for a routine oil change and lubrication, all work would usually stop, and everyone would come over and look at the machine. To many of the Mexicans it apparently meant that I was not a typical American. I was somehow different. And so I was treated in a different way.

The Mexican men have almost a reverence for well-designed machinery. Of all the people of Mexico, I noticed that the *Chiapanecos* seemed to be the most interested in the motorcycle. They gathered around wherever I stopped. I think this was because Chiapas is so isolated, and the men had never seen such a wondrous machine. There were times in remote areas when I was reminded of *A Connecticut Yankee in King Arthur's Court.*

A motorcycle is far superior to an automobile for the observance of nature. It was easy for me to stop to look at the freshly killed birds, snakes, and animals that lay by the roadside. I would also get off the bike in mid-desert to examine varieties of cacti. Exploring small roads in the jungle was a very rewarding activity. I would drive at a low speed. During the rainy season the trees almost completely cover the road, and it is like being at the bottom of a green canyon.

I was especially interested in the many species of hawks that I saw in Mexico. I have a lifelong interest in hawks, and they are probably my favorite birds. About fifty species of hawks and hawk-like birds are found in Mexico. If I saw one perched in a tree, I would always turn the motorcycle around and go back and look at it.

The gray fox, an intelligent and adaptable animal, is quite common throughout Mexico. I often spotted them from the motorcycle as they trotted along. Armadillos are also common in many parts of the country, and several times I spotted females with young. I immediately stopped the bike and tried to run them down on foot, but the animals are surprisingly elusive and always escaped in the underbrush.

There is really no way to communicate the joy and happiness that I experienced on my motorcycle trips. There is no way to describe the way I felt as I rode from one fine scene to another, under a blue sky on a warm and sunny day. The hotter the day, the more enjoyable it was, for I preferred to ride in shirtsleeves. Desert riding in shirtsleeves is exhilarating. My face and forearms were deeply tanned from the sun during the year I lived in Mexico, and I often wondered if I was more easily accepted by the people because my skin color was close to theirs.

I liked to explore the Mexican towns and villages on the motorcycle, taking slow rides down the quiet streets. It was also fun riding around the Mexican seaports. I would go very slowly, in first gear at about 2000 rpm, to see as much as I could see. It is the speed of a fast walk, and is a fine way to explore a port. At night I loved to take slow rides along the waterfront in the warm tropical air.

The reasons for liking motorcycles are partly subconscious, they are complicated and hard to explain. In myself I realized the connection with an interest in birds, a love of skiing, and past experience in flying. I also regarded a motorcycle as minimal. It was no more than I needed.

Motorcycles can be thought of as liberating machines. They help to free a person from many of the middle-class values and living standards that constrict him. The combination of the two experiences—a motorcycle, and Mexico—is a powerful force in this direction.

A motorcycle provides a remarkable combination of pain

and pleasure. There are hours of riding in cold rain, but then a twenty-minute hot shower in a hotel, followed by fresh clothing and a warm cafe. When traveling in a car these pleasures are lessened considerably. A motorcycle makes a person grateful for the simplest of comforts, essential things like shade and water. It is the ideal vehicle for an ascetic.

The medium-sized motorcycle that I owned was one of the new breed of motorcycles, powerful enough yet clean and quiet. It was a stock machine and not altered or modified in any way. I had no interest in speed. All I wanted was to be able to keep up with the traffic. A larger and heavier motorcycle was not really practical, since I had to frequently lift it into hotels and put it on trains. The motorcycle that I chose was able to carry me and a forty-pound load on a slight upgrade, against a moderate headwind, and easily keep up with the rest of the traffic. The engine was never straining. There are a number of medium-sized motorcycles on the market with enough power to do this.

Over the years I have ridden about 35,000 miles on motorcycles and have survived with ease. There was only one minor accident. The skilled and experienced motor-cyclist is not as defenseless as an automobile driver might think. The motorcycle provides unlimited visibility, is highly maneuverable, and has powerful brakes. The rider has his brain, his eyes and ears, a set of reflexes, perhaps even a sixth sense. Mostly it is his brain and judgement that keeps one motorcycle rider alive while another is killed.

On trips I found it vital to recognize fatigue, the point where physical reactions and mental processes are impaired. Then it was time to stop and rest, no matter where I was. I stayed well back from the vehicle in front of me, and always drove a little slower than I thought I could go. In addition I approached every intersection as though a car was about to come speeding through it, against the stop sign or red light. This kind of defensive driving is part of the art of staying alive.

It surprises me that many motorcycle riders do not even

know how to turn a corner properly. They are often out of control and could not handle a skid or a sudden-braking situation. In general, a motorcycle rider should go into a turn wider than he comes out of it. Most of the time he should brake, shift before the turn, and acccelerate through it.

A motorcycle can be stopped in a surprisingly short distance if the rider is not afraid to use maximum braking. I practiced maximum braking, using both the front and rear brakes, as a matter of routine. I did it every time I rode the bike. Most people do not realize it, but a motorcycle can be stopped in a shorter distance than a car. It requires more skill, however. I often hit the brakes when there was something I wanted to go back for, such as a hawk in a tree, a large snake crossing the road, or an armadillo with young.

Needless to say, riding a motorcycle in Mexico is not always fun. Various kinds of storms, including hurricanes, can make the weather miserable for days; several times on the central plateau I ran into terrific hailstorms and had to abandon the motorcycle and seek shelter; once on a dirt road during the rainy season, the motorcycle sank up to the license plates in mud; and it is no joy to have flying beetles, hard-bodied and weighing perhaps one-half ounce, smack into your forehead at sixty mph.

Because of the wind-chill factor, I was usually cold on a long drive if the temperature was below 55 degrees. On the plateau the temperature often drops much lower. For the motorcyclist, nothing quite compares with the exquisite experience of having a flat tire. Because there is no spare, a flat tire on a motorcycle is nothing less than a colossal pain in the ass. Lastly, I remember one time when I was riding at highway speed and a bee got into my shirt. In less than ten seconds I had the bike stopped and my shirt off. Talk about panic and frenzied activity!

In cities I was always glad to see a well-equipped machine shop, its doors and windows open to the street. If someday a motorcycle part was needed and was not available in Mexico, a machine shop was where it would be made. I seldom worried about things that might happen, such as mechanical breakdowns in remote areas. I had money with me, a command of Spanish, an appreciation for the absurd, a sense of humor, and an ability to solve problems. With those assets, there was nothing to fear.

Motorcycle Breaks

Because riding a motorcycle is more demanding, a rider must rest more often than the driver of a car. He also tends to drive at a lower speed and stops frequently. In a way these three characteristics are additional advantages of a motor-cycle, as a rider sees and experiences more.

I would usually take my breaks at small cafes, either on the road or in towns and villages. All the cafes provide a place to wash up, as it is the custom in Mexico. In rural areas it is often an outdoor washstand or open tap. Washing up is a necessity for the motorcycle rider, who is usually begrimed with road dust and diesel exhaust. In many of the simpler cafes you then take your own beer or soda pop from a cooler, drink it at a table, and pay at the end.

Sometimes I would be between towns when I felt like taking a break. But that was no problem. I wanted nothing more than water for washing, a place to sit in the shade, and a cold bottle of soda pop. Even the smallest country store or roadside stand had all these things. The places where I stopped for a break were usually the fronts of people's houses, and there were often cats, parrots, chickens scratching, birds in cages, or goats wandering about. Sometimes there were children playing, or a teenage daughter taking shy glances at me.

One time during a motorcycle break in Sinaloa I watched an old man cut up a deer he had shot. He sliced off thin strips of *venado* and hung them on a line to dry in the sun. I remember asking him where he had shot the deer. The old man said nothing, just pointed to the Sierra Madre in the distance. *"¿Usted?"* I asked, and pretended I was firing a rifle. *"Sí,"* he said.

In isolated parts of the Yucatán, where the villages are very small, the only place to take a break was the local corn mill, which is perhaps called the *molino*. It is where the women come every day to have their corn ground for making tortillas. These *molinos,* if they are called by that name, always had water for washing and soda pop for sale. I noticed that almost without exception the girls and women in these places wore white *huipiles,* the simple dress of the Yucatán. I liked the *huipiles* very much; they are graceful and feminine garments, and provide a nice contrast with the tan and brownish skin.

Motorcycle Trips

Down the east coast from the Texas border to Tamazunchale: the warm air, the increasing tropical vegetation, the Sierra Madre always to the west . . . . Children waving from the side of the road . . . . The ride from Tehuantepec at sea level up to San Cristóbal at 7000 feet . . . . From a cliffside road, the view of a village below: the broad expanse of red-tiled roofs . . . . The sight of the first wild parrot . . . . Tabasco: large areas of tropical savanna, with scattered patches of rainforest trees on the higher ground . . . . The longest trip was from Mexico City to Guatemala and back: 21 days, 1700 miles, 185 dollars . . . . Yucatán: the big sky . . . . The view of Santiago Tuxtla from above: the red-roofed little town set in a tropical valley, rimmed by green mountains . . . . Being on the road before dawn, when the sky is just becoming red in the east . . . . From above on the mountain road to Dolores Hidalgo: the magnificent view of Guanajuato, the surrounding mountains, and the plain beyond . . . . Vultures flying up from dead cattle . . . . Riding over the Toluca pass at 10,000 feet . . . . A fiesta day, *Cinco de Mayo:* flags, banners, festivities, Mexican bands, parades of schoolchildren in the villages I pass through . . . . Young women in small towns and villages who are so well dressed they could be in downtown Mexico City . . . . Near Lake Catemaco: the green tropical mountains in late-afternoon sunshine, a beautiful sight . . . . At the beginning of the day's ride, looking up at the sky like an airplane pilot or the captain of a fishing boat . . . . The acceleration when back on the open road after passing through a small village . . . . Stopping at the bridge in Tamazunchale to look down at the turquoise-colored Río Moctezuma . . . . Loading up the bike in the morning, sometimes surrounded by a small audience . . . . The descent into Orizaba, dropping thousands of feet in a few miles, and the fine views . . . . Everywhere I saw boys with slingshots . . . . Zooming over the last ridge of hills and seeing Acapulco spread out below . . . . The lush tropics during the rainy season between Mazatlán and San Blas . . . . Stopping the motorcycle by the side of the road to watch the planting of corn . . . . The six-hour ride from Tehuantepec: over the last ridge, and there is the valley of Oaxaca . . . . The motorcycle trip as a unit of experience . . . . Crossing the Tropic of Cancer . . . . The inexpressible joy when starting out in the morning, on a beautiful day in scenic country . . . . Approaching Veracruz from the hot coastal plain: a cool breeze, a salty smell, then the sight of the Gulf . . . . A bare-breasted woman washing clothes in a tropical stream . . . . The Michoacán countryside, green and lush during the summertime . . . . Small boys chasing an armadillo in a field . . . . The magnificent cumulus and cumulonimbus clouds that form along the Gulf coast . . . . A spirited herd of horses with several foals . . . . I liked to observe the changes in vegetation that occur during ascents and descents . . . . I usually noticed the appearance but not the disappearance of vegetation types . . . . Written on the back of an old and very slow truck: *cuál es la prisa* or what is the hurry . . . . South of Ciudad Valles, three successive mountain-lines in the distance, each one a lighter color; atmospheric perspective the painters call it . . . . The hot road glistening wet from a sudden shower, with wisps of water vapor rising . . . . The scenic and winding descent from cool Zimapán on the plateau down to warm Tamazunchale . . . . The sudden rise in temperature when I passed through some cuts in mountain roads . . . . The signs at the borders of states appealed to me: leaving Michoacán, entering Jalisco; leaving Tabasco, entering Chiapas; etc. etc. . . . . Passing through a pretty village sparkling with dew in the morning sun . . . . The wide-faced Indians along the roadside in the Huasteca country, many of them indistinguishable from Chinese . . . . Border trip, Querétaro to Laredo and back: 8 days, 1000 miles, 75 dollars . . . . Leaving Zitácuaro early in the morning: deserted cobblestone streets, many columns of smoke, pine-smell in the air . . . . Stopping the motorcycle by the side of the road to observe how adobe bricks are made . . . . Seeing the distant Pacific Ocean from the mountains of Chiapas . . . . Riding slowly through cloud forest, and stopping to examine orchids and giant ferns . . . . The rugged green mountains approaching the Guatemala border . . . . Tropical lagoons filled with violet flowers . . . . The smell from behind a truck loaded with strawberries . . . . Michoacán: tiny villages of red-roofed houses clustered together . . . . Riding on a desert road in Sonora, with views of the Gulf of California . . . . Coasting with the engine off down a narrow jungle road . . . . *Campesinos* along the roadside in the Yucatán, carrying ancient single-barreled shotguns . . . . Riding at sunset on the west coast: violet sky, ghostly coconut groves, blue mountain ridges . . . . Cattle crossing a flooded stream, up to their bellies in water . . . . The winding road down to San Blas, with patches of jungle and medium-height rainforest . . . . A flock of green parrots, squawking as they fly . . . . Stopping at a coconut-milk stand in a grove of trees beside a tropical river . . . . Zitácuaro to Morelia: the road winding through small volcanic cones covered with green vegetation . . . . Down the west coast:

Guaymas, Ciudad Obregón, Navojoa, Los Mochis, Culiacán, Mazatlán, San Blas . . . . A remote village in Guerrero: twenty children standing in a circle around the motorcycle and looking at it . . . . The road from Mexico City to Cuernavaca: from the cold pine-covered mountains, the view of the warm valley of Morelos below . . . . All over Mexico, and especially in the Yucatán, I saw those galvanized metal windmills made by the Aermotor Company of Chicago . . . . Railroad siding: a line of old boxcars used as housing, several of them freshly painted and adorned with flower boxes . . . . CN-195 in Chiapas: climbing higher and higher and then finally entering the level of the clouds . . . . A large plantation on the west coast with mixed rows of banana trees and coconut palms . . . . Stopping on a ridge to watch coastal rains sweeping across the green jungle below . . . . Mexican cowboys on horseback with rifles slung on the saddles . . . . The colorful town of Alvarado on the Gulf coast: fishing boats and many cafes on the bank of the broad Río Papaloapan . . . . A black sow and six black piglets crossing a sand bar in a tropical river . . . . The night ride around Acapulco Bay in the warm air . . . . Sonora desert: blue sky, cumulus clouds, mountains in the distance . . . .

National Museum of Anthropology

Almost everyone agrees that the National Museum of Anthropology in Mexico City is one of the finest museums in the world. I only wish that it was not so big, for it takes at least two or three trips to see it properly. It should really be two museums with separate locations: one of anthropology, the other of ethnology.

From a museum of the right size, I usually come away with a good feeling. But from one that is too large, I leave bleary-eyed and fatigued. An example of a properly-sized building is the new historical museum, spiral-shaped like the

Guggenheim in New York, which is located below Chapultepec castle. It is officially called the Gallery of the Independence. The United States would do well to copy this smart little museum, in both style and scale, to depict its own history.

The National Museum of Anthropology contains many colorful and imaginative paintings that re-create scenes from the past. There is a marvelous painting of a group of Pleistocene animals; a painting that depicts a group of Asians crossing the Bering land-bridge many thousands of years ago; and a huge panorama-painting of ancient Tenochtitlán. I have looked at these and others in the museum for long periods of time. The artists who researched and laboriously painted them have done what no photographer can do.

There is a fine model of an Aztec market in the museum. I remember looking with special interest at the section of the market that sold snakes, iguanas, and armadillos. There is also a model of the Valley of Mexico at the height of the Aztec civilization. It shows the two snow-capped volcanoes, Popocatépetl and Ixtaccíhuatl, on the rim; the Aztec city of Tenochtitlán in the center; the ancient Lake Texcoco, with the bridges and causeways to the city; and orchards and fields of corn on the lower slopes of the mountains.

I was surprised that a room in the museum was not devoted to killings and human sacrifices. It would probably be the most popular exhibit. They could have dioramas of the Aztecs cutting out the heart of a captured warrior; a dishonest official being flayed alive; the Mayas tossing a young girl into the sacred well; and the leader of a winning ball team decapitating the leader of the losing team.

My favorite diorama is the one that depicts the mammoth-hunting scene. A group of prehistoric hunters have surrounded a mammoth in a swamp, and are fighting it with spears in a fierce and bloody struggle. "Why is this superb creation not considered art?" I once asked a friend who is an artist. After some thought she said, "Because it does not contain a personal statement." I suppose she is right.

Nevertheless I would rather look at that splendid diorama than 95 per cent of the paintings and sculptures I have seen.

Night Ride

I once took a ride on the motorcycle on a warm summer night in the Sonora desert outside Guaymas. It was before I learned that it is dangerous to drive in Mexico at night. Fortunately the road was a minor one, rather isolated, and there were no other vehicles. The month was August, the time about an hour after sunset, and the desert air was still quite warm.

This night ride is an unforgettable experience in my memory. The air was dry and smelled of the desert vegetation, and it was still warm enough to ride in shirtsleeves. I remember that the eyeshine of a few desert animals, who are most active at night, was caught in the headlight. The motorcycle appeared to be transformed in a marvelous way. It was only an illusion, but the bike sounded better, the tone of the engine was deeper, and it seemed bigger and more powerful.

At one point I stopped the motorcycle by the side of the road. I shut off the ignition, took off my riding glasses, and smelled-looked-listened. It was absolutely quiet. I was all alone on that part of the Sonora desert, listening for sounds, inhaling the warm good-smelling air. I remember that I could see the desert vegetation nearby, the bright stars overhead, and the outlines of the mountains in the distance.

Opinions and Observations

Many of the Mexicans may be slight in stature, but they are often surprisingly strong. A few times, when being helped to move the motorcycle into a hotel, I was amazed to see a skinny little man lift the heavy end right off the ground . . . . *Frijoles de olla,* whole beans in their own juice, are much better than *frijoles refritos* . . . . Mexican subsidiaries of American companies do not necessarily consist of efficient south-of-the-border branches of the American firm. They are Mexican companies and are often run in a screwed-up Mexican way. This is not a reckless or anti-Mexican statement, this is the truth . . . . After being among Indians for a while, such as in the villages near San Cristóbal, being back among the regular Mexicans makes them seem almost like brothers . . . . Mexican pastry is all promise . . . . Because of the amusement and diversion that we Americans provide for the Mexicans, I think they should set aside a holiday for us. They could call it *Gringo Day* . . . . It is a misconception to think that you must go deep into the country to find the real Mexico. Totally Mexican communities are often within a few miles of the border . . . . People with a tenuous grip on their mental health should not visit Mexico . . . . I would rather be a poor Mexican boy in Acapulco than in any other place . . . . There are millions of wristwatches in Mexico, but few clocks in public view . . . . It is not true that the Mexicans are trying to drive you crazy, it only seems that way . . . . The great sadness in so many of the Mexican faces; each one in his own isolation . . . . I would guess that few women in Mexico have a satisfactory sex life . . . . The time of year, and specifically the amount of rainfall, is a major factor in the appearance of the countryside. There are really two Mexicos, quite different: the Mexico of the dry season, and the Mexico of the rainy season . . . . Elevator operators often decorate and personalize the little areas where they stand; bus drivers do the same thing to their dashboards . . . . Some of the people in remote areas were afraid of me, or at least very shy. Several times in Chiapas, when I stopped the motorcycle to ask an Indian directions, he ran away in fright. And if he did not run away, he often spoke only his Indian tongue and knew no Spanish . . . . Height is often an indication of social class . . . . The Mexican postage stamps are generally superior in design to those of the United States, but they are inferior to those of Spain and Italy . . . . Girls and women in Mexico were rarely interested in the motorcycle. Such machines were part of the world of men, and that was that . . . . The way the Mexicans use color always interested me. They recklessly intermix both pastels and bright colors . . . . Small children die in Mexico when a few dollars' worth of antibiotics could save them . . . . From inside, some one-story houses appear to be nothing more than large patios, with rooms constructed around the perimeters. The centers of the houses are entirely open to the sky . . . . Many of the Mexicans have a grudging respect for the way Americans travel in their country. "They go everywhere," a Mexican man once said to me, "they have no fear" . . . . The standard of living called voluntary poverty in the United States is a rather comfortable standard of living in Mexico . . . . It is not unusual to hear roosters crowing in the downtown areas of large cities . . . . At roasting-hot Uxmal and Chitchén Itzá, I remember seeing female tourists with large sweat-patches under their arms. Somehow it pleases me to see women sweating like men . . . . If you want to read books about Mexico, especially histories, there are so many written that it is possible to read until you go blind . . . . The area on tropical coasts where the beach meets the jungle has always fascinated me . . . . It is no tragedy when a picturesque village in the mountains or a fishing village on the coast is "discovered" and inundated with tourists. There are hundreds of other villages, some of them effectively isolated by unpaved roads or no roads at all, that are still unspoiled . . . . An old Mexican moviehouse on a chilly night is a fine setting for a horror film . . . . I now understand why foreigners have often done a lot of drinking when living in the tropics . . . . Many species of birds and animals are doomed in Mexico, and many fine areas will be lost forever unless they are set aside as national parks or wildlife refuges. The situation is extremely depressing to anyone interested in conservation . . . . I never was enthusiastic about tortillas, except when I was fiercely hungry or there was a good sauce in which to dip them. The food value of tortillas is relatively low, but perhaps this will be changed in the future with the increased use of protein supplements and high-lysine corn . . . . In almost every town there are Orientals of some kind, most often Chinese . . . . I always liked to see women nursing their babies in Mexico. It is quite splendid, I responded to it many times. I admit that I always eyeballed nursing mothers . . . . Many of the well-dressed students in Mexico City are actually impoverished and live in tiny furnished rooms called *cuartitos* . . . . I would love to see certain species of African antelopes introduced to parts of Mexico, in what are called "unfilled ecological niches" . . . . It is heartening that the Mexicans look towards the advanced societies of Europe for ideas as much as to the United States . . . . When I lived in the *azotea,* I remember that the Señora would put a hen under a bucket to make it lay an egg. Is this done all over Mexico? . . . . Just as the American language developed until it became superior to English, so has Mexican Spanish become superior to the language of Spain. James Norman describes Mexican Spanish as "richer, more flexible and elegant . . . softer and more euphonious." He also mentions the thousands of Indian words that have enriched the language in the New World . . . . Some of the histories of Mexico are horrifying and depressing to read because of the accounts of brutality, torture, and murder . . . . Like many third-world countries, Mexico has an inadequate and disappointing approach to population control . . . . I sometimes envied the American girls who had Mexican boyfriends, for they had knowledgeable guides who could give them much information. Many times I wanted to ask a Mexican friend, "What is this? What is happening here?" . . . . A trip to the Gulf coast and the Yucatán during the month of May, when it is incredibly hot and humid, made me greatly appreciate the climate of the west coast, which is far superior . . . . The Mexicans of German origin are sometimes a strange mixture of the Teutonic and the Latin . . . . The Mexicans stared at my shoes so often that after a while I was staring at them myself . . . . In general I went along with the Mexican habits and customs in regards to food. When in Rome, etc. But there are limits, and a foreigner must draw the line at certain practices. I did not care for the Mexican customs of putting lime juice on almost everything; of having beans at the end of the meal; and of putting chili on almost everything, including fresh fruit . . . . Sometimes the favorable reputation of a town in Mexico is essentially false. It is mostly due to years of press agentry and public relations by the leading hotels and other tourism interests . . . . Young men go to the university, obtain a degree, begin their careers and professional lives, yet often continue to live at home with their parents the entire time . . . . I heard that American girls should be careful in areas where there is guerrilla activity. The danger is apparently not from the guerrillas, but from the Mexican soldiers who are also in the areas . . . . At one point in *Burmese Days,* George Orwell allows himself to say, "Orientals can be very irritating." There were times when I wondered what he would have said about the Mexicans . . . . The torture of Cuauhtémoc seems to be a favorite subject for artists and illustrators . . . . The entire border area is so atypical of either the United States or Mexico that it is almost like a third country . . . . I liked the Mexicans well enough, but the Spanish in Mexico were even better. They are surely among the finest people in the world . . . . I liked to observe the various stages in the fattening process that afflicts many Mexican females. It begins with cute but plump teenagers and ends with the formidable two-hundred-pound señoras who often outweigh their husbands . . . . International politics: to the typical Mexican it is not government vs. government but *hombre* vs. *hombre* . . . . Mexico is more elemental and more foreign than any

119

country in Europe . . . . Some psychologists pair *machismo* in Mexican men with the martyr complex in Mexican women . . . . Many of the horror stories about Mexico are nothing more than unfounded rumors. Many of them are either completely false or greatly exaggerated. But some of the most incredible ones are absolutely true . . . . The Mexican as a new race is in a sense more advanced than the American, for he is closer to the multi-racial "world man" that will eventually predominate on this planet . . . .

Owls

On Calle Lopez in Mexico City there is an *óptica* or eyeglasses shop called *Los Dos Buhos,* which means The Two Owls. And outside the shop, on high perches above the sidewalk, are two great horned owls. I passed them many times on my way to the San Juan Market or the Metro station, and always stopped and exchanged stares with them. They would glare down at me, both of them fine-looking birds, with huge yellow eyes and serious fierce expressions. The owner of the *óptica* shop was probably an astute businessman who was well aware that many of his countrymen and their children loved birds. Inside the shop I could usually see a third owl, which I imagine was a spare.

Palenque

The town of Palenque, which is a short distance from the famed ruins, has immense tourist potential, and will probably be unrecognizable in a few years. The ruins themselves are my favorites in Mexico, even though the best relics and objects of art have long ago been taken away to museums and private collections. In contrast to the Maya ruins on the flat

Yucatán peninsula, the ruins at Palenque have a magnificent site. They are set among green jungle-covered hills and luxuriant vegetation.

After it was abandoned and overgrown with jungle, Palenque was often called City of Snakes by Indians in the area. I remember that I saw a long green snake, a beautiful creature, making its way among the fallen building-stones. The area is often terribly hot and humid, especially in May, and the visitor to Palenque must walk slowly and rest frequently in the shade. I noticed how my speed increased as I progressed through the ruins, how I saw less and sweated more.

There is a good view of the ruins and the tropical lowlands beyond from the top of the most impressive temple. I liked sitting at the top of this temple and imagining Palenque at two times: at the height of its civilization, and at the time of its discovery as a "lost city". The visitor of ruins must bring imagination and some background information with him, or the experience will be much less rewarding. I had read a description of Palenque when it was first discovered. It was then overgrown with jungle and luxuriant vegetation, and was truly a lost city. The early accounts must have been exciting to the Englishmen and Europeans of the 18th century who read about them. The lost cities of tropical America!

There is some fine rainforest, with paths for walking, on the slope behind the most impressive temple. It is suitable habitat for the two types of monkeys that are native to Mexico, the howler and the spider. I listened and looked into the treetops but did not see or hear any. This jungle area is one of the outstanding attractions of Palenque. Where else in Mexico can you walk on paths in virgin rainforest? When I was there I found a jungle glade that was ideal, with lianas, air plants, giant trees with fluted trunks, and everything else. I remember sitting quietly in this lovely glade for a long time, looking into the treetops, and listening to the fascinating variety of jungle sounds.

Pescadería

I once encountered a large and busy *pescaderia* in Veracruz on a walk one Saturday morning. Three young men were cleaning a variety of fish with incredible speed and skill. I purchased nothing, just wandered around and observed the whole operation. There were many people and no one paid any attention to me.

I looked closely at a number of ice-filled bins that contained different types of fish from the Gulf. Signs gave the name of the fish in Spanish and the price in pesos per kilo. There were strange-looking fish I had never seen, and also sea bass, pompano, skate, octopus, squid, red snapper, butterfish, shark, mackerel, shrimp, and barracuda. It was like a visit to an aquarium, but better in a way, because I was so close to the fish.

Customers selected their fish, paid for them at a cash register, and then had them cleaned by the young men. I noticed that it was the custom to leave a small tip. Never have I seen fish cleaned so rapidly, and I stood there for ten minutes or more, unable to leave, watching the flashing knives and choppers.

Plaza

One of the most attractive aspects of a Mexican town is the public plaza at the center. I spent many hours just sitting in plazas when I lived in Mexico. I would sit quietly, calm and happy and content, listening to the periodic churchbells, looking at the sky and the trees and the passing people.

I remember thinking about the wisdom of those who drafted the old Spanish laws for the establishment of towns, who knew that a town should be centered around a public plaza. They also wisely provided for one side of the plaza to be reserved for public buildings. Most of the towns and villages in Mexico are laid out according to old Spanish law.

I considered it an achievement, for someone of my background, to be able to sit quietly in a plaza and do absolutely nothing. When I lived in Mexico I had the time for such a worthwhile activity. Sitting in the plaza I had the time to think about the really important things, such as the differences between morning sunshine and afternoon sunshine. I would often stay long enough in the plaza to observe' the movement of the shadows. Sometimes I stayed long enough to perceive the temperature change as the sun dropped lower in the sky.

Political Notes

Mexico is still dependent upon large amounts of foreign capital, most of it from the United States.... I was told that if someone reports a murder in Mexico, he may be held by the police until he proves that he is innocent. Can such a thing be true? . . . . There may be social-welfare programs in Mexico for government employees and other large groups, but for most other Mexicans it is still the same old struggle for existence . . . . Mexico has some disturbing characteristics of a police state . . . . Many Mexicans and foreign residents are reluctant to talk about certain subjects, for example the massacre at Tlatelolco. The reasons can range from a vague sense of prudence to outright fear. In Mexico the midnight knock on the door is a reality, although repression is usually accomplished in more subtle and patient ways. Arbitrary and capricious harassment over a period of time is very effective . . . . Many aspects of Emiliano Zapata's *Plan de Ayala* for an agrarian revolution in Mexico are sound today . . . . I often wondered about the extent of CIA involvement in Mexico. How many agents are assigned there? How much money is spent? What exactly is done? . . . . At this time the more progressive elements of the Mexican government favor a market economy within a planned framework, somewhat like the Yugoslavian system . . . . Simplistic explanations of Mexican politics are not really possible, for the political situation is extremely complex. Even well-informed people in Mexico City are in continual disagreement over what is happening in their own country . . . . If sadistic gorillas exist in the police and military of certain South American countries, they surely can be found in Mexico. I would not believe any indignant denials by officials of the Mexican government. The interrogators and torturers might speak Spanish with a different accent, but they would be cut from the same Latin-American cloth of fascism and righteous *machismo* . . . . Although there is much socialist rhetoric, Mexico remains intensely capitalist. The free-enterprise scramble is most evident on the streets and in the markets . . . . At this time the Mexican government does not even pretend to call Mexico a democracy. At most it is described as a democracy in formation, which also helps to justify certain totalitarian practices . . . . I once spent an evening in the house of a prominent Mexican family. They were charming and attractive people, I liked them, they were extremely nice to me, I enjoyed myself very much. But I did happen to overhear several political comments, and also observed a few other things. Afterwards I realized that such an attractive scene was also an aspect of fascism in Latin America . . . .In regards to the Mexican government and their leftist and guerrilla opponents, it is not unreasonable to suspect, especially after having seen *State of Siege,* that horrible tortures take place in certain soundproofed cellars in Mexico City . . . . Memorable scenes from *State of Siege:* interrogating the terrified girl who had a large bruise above her eye; the closeups of electrode-torture of the naked man; the three police hoods beating and then killing the leftist student . . . . Americans who are used to due process, civil liberties, the Bill of Rights, and everything else in the police stations and courtrooms of the United States are often shocked at the way things are done in Mexico . . . . I was told that during 1968,

124

when the Mexican government was extremely concerned about the effects of demonstrations upon the Olympics, a number of people simply disappeared and were never heard of again . . . . Any Marxist analysis of the social-economic-political situation in Mexico becomes almost an academic exercise due to the overwhelming presence of the United States. Of course this statement could also have been made for Cuba in 1958. . . . Article 33 of the Mexican constitution provides that "undesirable aliens", which are often American tourists, can be immediately deported for any reason and without appeal . . . . I sometimes wondered what they do when they capture a guerrilla in Mexico. Do they ask him politely for information? Do they inform him of his rights? . . . . You won't see any murals by Mexican artists that depict the massacre at Tlatelolco . . . . The United States Embassy in Mexico City is well designed in one respect, for it is "hardened". The facade is mostly marble and concrete, and the windows are few and rather small. If a crowd of students attacks the Embassy, as has happened in the past, damage will not be extensive . . . .

Portales

Some of the provincial cities in Mexico, such as Celaya, Uruapan, Mérida, Oaxaca, Puebla, Veracruz, and Morelia, have *portales* that face on the plaza. These are shaded arcade-like walkways that at certain times are filled with people and busy with activity. Most of them have magazine stands, fast-food windows, and vendors of all kinds. The cafes located under the *portales* usually put out tables and chairs, and it is often a pleasant and interesting place.

I loved to sit at a table under the *portales* and drink coffee and observe the activity. The early evening was my favorite time. Except in tourist towns, most of the other tables would be occupied by middle-class Mexican men of all ages. In many ways it was the center of town for them. They would be smoking, drinking various beverages, reading the newspaper, playing dominoes and board games, and talking among themselves. I overheard many of the conversations, and they tirelessly discussed the same subjects that men discuss in provincial cities around the world. I was reminded of a description by Camus of a similar scene in the city of Oran in Algeria.

The tables under the *portales* are a good place to sit and talk with a companion, to drink a beer or *café con leche,* and to sit and watch the late-afternoon rainstorm. During the rain a diverse collection of people seeks shelter under the *portales.* The cafes usually fill up, and the mix of people is interesting to observe. Many aspects of life under the *portales* appealed to me. I appreciated the activity, the random encounters, the view of the plaza, the exposure to the weather, and the variety of the people. It was pleasant and stimulating at the same time. I can think of no real equivalent to the *portales* in the United States.

Many of the cafes have expresso machines and serve cappuccino. I have always thought that cappuccino is a very civilized drink. It is another gift that the Italians have given to the world. Cappuccino is very popular with the Mexicans, especially the young men and women, and I always had it when it was available. Cappuccino under the *portales* while looking out on a plaza in Mexico is a fine blending of the Old and New Worlds.

Postcards

The Mexicans that I met on my motorcycle trips occasionally gave me little gifts. They were inconsequential items, without any real value, but gifts just the same. Naturally I needed something to give in return. I therefore carried a supply of picture postcards with me whenever I traveled in

Mexico. I gave them to various people, sometimes children and teenagers, at times when it was appropriate. The postcards were all the same, a beautiful color photograph of San Francisco as seen from above the Marin end of the Golden Gate Bridge. I told them that it was where I was from in the United States. Some of the girls and women reacted to the lovely view of the city with exclamations like: "¡Oh! ¡Qué bonita!"

Preferences

From the time that I lived and traveled in Mexico, I have compiled this list of preferences. Most of these will surely change in time, but at the moment, here they are. Favorite small plaza: the Jardín de la Union in Guanajuato. Favorite states: Veracruz, Oaxaca, and Chiapas. Favorite seaside resort: still Acapulco, although most will disagree. Favorite university: none, the universities are disappointing. Favorite red wine: *Noblejo*. It is light and smooth, comparable to a good claret. Best train ride: Chihuahua to Los Mochis. Best post office: Oaxaca. Favorite large patio: the one in Bellas Artes, a run-down former monastery in San Miguel de Allende. Favorite statue: the Diana on the Paseo de la Reforma in Mexico City. Favorite pottery: the greenish-glaze from Michoacán. Favorite highway: the scenic CN-195, from Villahermosa to near San Cristóbal de las Casas. Favorite large plazas: the ones in Puebla, Morelia, and Oaxaca. Favorite coastal town: Campeche, still quiet and unspoiled. Favorite cheeses: locally-made *queso de Oaxaca,* usually called *quesillo* there, and also *queso de Chihuahua*. Favorite town with many Americans: at this time, San Miguel de Allende, although there are many tourists and it is relatively expensive. Favorite all-around place: Mexico City, although most will disagree. Favorite bookstore: the Librería Anglo-Americana in Mexico City, with its fine stock of

Penguin Books. Best English-language library: the Biblioteca Benjamin Franklin in Mexico City. Favorite small library: the Biblioteca Publica in San Miguel de Allende. Favorite basketry: that made by the Seri Indians of Sonora. Favorite small cities: the state capitals of Morelia and Querétaro. Also Oaxaca, although the reaction to some of the young Americans has made it less pleasant. Favorite park: the beautiful Parque Nacional in Uruapan.

Prostitutes

In Mexico City I was friendly with an English journalist who spoke Spanish fluently and knew the city well. He liked to drink and I sometimes went with him to bars in the downtown area. He was fond of an after-hours bar on Calle Bolivar, a place where you had to knock and identify yourself to be admitted. It had a colorful assortment of Mexicans and Spanish exiles, some of whom seemed to operate on the fringes of the law.

Prostitutes and other customers began to arrive at around nine or ten o'clock in the evening. Three or four a.m. was the peak time, and the place was filled. I already knew that prostitutes were common in many Mexican bars, and I liked seeing them, as they added something to the atmosphere. They definitely interested me. I would look at their faces, bodies, and clothes, and observe the way they operated in the bar. My journalist friend knew a couple of them, and occasionally they sat at our table and had a drink.

Pulmonías

Only in Mazatlán did I see three-wheeled motorscooter taxis, although they may exist in other Mexican cities. These taxis are funny-looking little vehicles. Their putt-putt sound is heard everywhere and is part of the ambience of Mazatlán. Because these taxis are open to the air, the Mexicans call them *pulmonías,* which literally means pneumonias.

Pulmonías are great fun, especially if you and your companion have had a couple of drinks. I always liked to see the little vehicles careening around the corners in Mazatlán. Many of the drivers are skilled and reckless at the same time. Perhaps it is my imagination, but they seem to have a special spirit that is lacked by the drivers of ordinary taxis.

Most of the *pulmonías* are named for women. Painted on them are names like *Teresa, Cecilia, Alicia, Isabel, Maria, Claudia, Julieta,* and *Felicia.* If only they were battery-powered, such vehicles would make good warm-weather taxis for the downtown areas of American cities.

Rainforest

Wildlife of Mexico by A. Starker Leopold, published by the University of California Press, is an outstanding book. In it are good descriptions of the different vegetation zones of Mexico. Leopold describes, and locates with a multi-colored map, the various types: savanna, cloud forest, desert, mangrove swamp, tropical rainforest, mesquite-grassland, thorn forest, chaparral, tropical scrub, pine-oak forest, and others. Of all these, one particular type has always fascinated me: the tropical rainforest.

In Mexico I was most interested in the classic example of this, what is often described as high rainforest, with the tallest trees. It is also where the most interesting wildlife is to be found. Anyone who has responded to the writings of Joseph Conrad and W. H. Hudson can understand a fascination with this type of forest. The difficulty is that high rainforest is not easy to encounter in Mexico, for most of it has been cut down. It is depressing to see the expanses of savanna and tropical scrub and secondary forest where virgin stands of rainforest once existed.

In areas that have been cleared for agriculture, an occasional rainforest tree is sometimes left standing, perhaps to provide shade for the field workers to rest. The big trees are lonely reminders of the magnificent rainforest that once covered the land. I often stopped the motorcycle by the side of the road and admired these strange-looking trees, many of them with fluted trunks, some of them supporting lianas, orchids, and air plants. The giant trees looked as though they had come from another planet, perhaps a great Venusian swamp, or else were survivors from our own Pleistocene era.

There are no paved roads, as far as I know, that lead to the best areas of rainforest. You must hike or have a four-wheel-drive vehicle or rent horses and a guide or be flown in by a small plane. I saw patches and small areas of rainforest, most of it of only medium height, in an area near Tamazunchale; near San Andrés Tuxtla and Lake Catemaco; at the ruins of Palenque; and from the Mérida-Mexico City train, between Tenosique and Teapa. I remember that it looked green and spongy from a distance, incredibly lush, like no forest I have ever seen.

In *Wildlife of Mexico*, Leopold suggests a promising site for a national park that will preserve the rainforest habitat. It is the northeastern slope of Volcán San Martín Tuxtla in southern Veracruz. Areas of rainforest to the southeast, in Tabasco, Campeche, Chiapas, and Quintana Roo, are more extensive. The department of Petén in Guatemala, which is just across the border from Mexico, has some of the finest rainforest in the Western Hemisphere. On a map of Guatemala I was once intrigued by an enormous area without any paved roads. It was simply labeled "Jungles of El Petén".

The Mexican government ought to set aside a national park to preserve this unique type of forest, and make it accessible to those who are interested. There should be accommodations nearby, pathways to walk on, perhaps an exhibit of the birds and animals that are found in the rainforest. In time, this national park could become like our Yellowstone and Yosemite. It could become one of the outstanding attractions of Mexico, with great importance for its people, and draw visitors from all over the world.

Reading

For the person who believes in self-education through independent reading, Mexico is an ideal place to live. There is all the time to read good books that anyone could desire. I probably did more real reading in Mexico in one year than many college students are able to do in four. And they were books that I wanted to read, not books that I had to read. What a difference there is!

In Mexico I had the time to read H. W. Fowler's *Modern English Usage,* and also H. L. Mencken's *American Language.* I read the King James version of the Bible, many pages at a sitting. I was able to spend many hours browsing at random through the *Encyclopedia Brittanica.* The article on Mexico, by the way, was excellent, and packed with information. I read it twice and recommend it to anyone going to Mexico.

When I lived in the village I would leisurely look through the atlas in the *biblioteca,* going over the maps of the countries, reading the names of the rivers and mountain ranges. I read the almanac, which is surprisingly good reading, from beginning to end. I even read an abridged dictionary. I read it for ten or fifteen minutes at a time, stopping as soon as I felt fatigue.

Some of the books I read in Mexico are *The Journal of Delacroix,* the essays of Ralph Waldo Emerson, *White Collar* by C. Wright Mills, the complete works of both Nathanael West and Lewis Carroll, *The Gallery* by John Horne Burns, all of Orwell that was in Penguin, *Two Cheers for Democracy* by E. M. Forster, the complete essays of Montaigne (translated by Donald Frame, in three volumes), *Walden* by Thoreau, *Leaves of Grass* by Walt Whitman, *Experiment in Autobiography* by H. G. Wells, and *The Voyage of the Beagle* by Charles Darwin, edited by Leonard Engel.

In addition to these I had the time to read scores of other books, mostly poetry and short stories and novels. I remember thinking that books become far more valuable when one is living in a country like Mexico. Many books were not available there, so I returned to the United States with a three-page list of books and articles to look up in the library. I still have that list, with most of the entries crossed out. It contains items that are amusing to me now, such as:

Goldman, E. A. (1943). "The Races of the Ocelot and Margay in Middle America." *Journal Mammalia* 24:372–385.

I discovered that Mexico provides a fine setting to read books about Spain, such as *Homage to Catalonia* by George Orwell and *For Whom the Bell Tolls* by Ernest Hemingway. I read them both when I lived in Mexico, and the place where they were read definitely enhanced the experience of the books. I also remember how I felt when walking on the streets of the village after a session of reading; conversely, these books enhanced the experience of Mexico.

Another book about Spain that is not so well known, but delightful and beautifully written, is *As I Walked Out One Midsummer Morning* by Laurie Lee. It is a personal account of a 20-year-old poet traveling through Spain in 1935–36. The book is youthful, charming, and exuberant, written with high spirits, and filled with memorable lines. It is one of my favorite travel books, although it is also classified as autobiography.

In the *biblioteca* were also stacks of old magazines, and I spent many an afternoon looking through them. I can almost imagine a university course entitled *Old Magazines*. The back issues of *Life* magazine were most appealing, where the photographs showed fashions that are now humorous to recall, celebrities and public figures that are now forgotten or dead. I read about the rise and fall of ideas, morals, and politics over three generations. The afternoons spent looking through those old magazines, in the almost timeless setting of rural Mexico, deepened my perspective. It made me more aware of how transitory are the things I read about, of what time does to issues, events, and people.

Reforma

One time I was on the Paseo de la Reforma early in the morning, on my way to take a bus to the downtown area. There was no smog, traffic was light, and pretty girls were walking by on their way to work. I was in a fine mood, happy and content. At the bus stop I sat down on a bench and waited. When I eventually saw a bus approaching, I was actually disappointed, for I did not want to leave. Suddenly it occurred to me that I could remain sitting and let the bus go by. I did that, and with the next one, too. Altogether I let three or four go by. And why not? My errands in downtown Mexico City could wait, and I was perfectly happy sitting there.

Reforma Hotels Part I

When I lived in Mexico City I often wandered through the luxury hotels on the Paseo de la Reforma that catered to American tourists. I would look at the people in the lobbies, walk through the air-conditioned bars, browse at the magazine stands, explore the various restaurants. The staff probably took me for an American student whose parents were guests of the hotel.

I generally disliked the hotels themselves, for a number of reasons. One was the plush and formal atmosphere. Another was that I always saw the most horrible Americans in these hotels. And it was depressing to see Mexican men in uniforms at the beck and call of Americans. What it eventually does to the Mexican men is painful to observe. In general, the greater the social distance between hotel employees and guests, the less I liked a Mexican hotel.

A few of the hotels on Reforma had pleasant coffeeshops, however, and I would sometimes have coffee there in the afternoons. I liked to overhear the tourists talking about Mexico; it was often amusing to hear of Americans encountering the Mexican way of doing things. It was also a pleasure to hear English spoken, in the various accents of the United States. Sometimes it made me feel slightly homesick, and I would contemplate returning. I would dream of whole cities of English-speaking people, and American movies everywhere.

Reforma Hotels Part II

When I visited the hotels I often took the elevators to the roofs, where I saw many fine views in all directions. If it was a clear day I could see the entire Valley of Mexico, including the snow-capped volcanoes Ixtaccíhuatl and Popocatépetl. It is not always hazy or smoggy in the capital; Mexico City has some of the finest blue-sky days, with ideal temperatures, to be found anywhere. They occur most often on Sundays. There are still times, although they are rare, when the visibility is unlimited, and I could then see the volcanoes as clearly as the Aztecs saw them.

The tip-off was when the detail on the nearby hills was clearly visible from the street. Then I knew it was worthwhile to take a trip to the top of a hotel. The volcanoes were sometimes hidden by clouds, but the mountains to the north, south, and west were usually sharp and clear. The evening view of Mexico City and the surrounding mountains is one of the most spectacular in the world.

Not all the hotels have restaurants and pools on the rooftops. Some are relatively bare, with only enclosed machinery and storage areas, and they were actually my favorites. Many times I was alone on the roof of a tall hotel along the Paseo de la Reforma, responding to the magnificent panorama. One of the best times was just as the lights of Mexico City were beginning to come on. At this time the snow-capped peaks of Ixtaccíhuatl and Popocatépetl are often rosy-bright in the last sunlight.

Rolf

One afternoon in Mexico City I was walking along the busy Avenida Bucareli, in the neighborhood where several of the newspaper offices are located. Outside the Cafe Habana, which is frequented by Mexican journalists and newspaper people, I noticed a parked BMW motorcycle, battered and muddy. I looked it over and saw that it had 87,000 kilometers on it. At this point the owner of the BMW, a man in his early thirties, came out from the Cafe Habana. We started talking in Spanish, but when I found out that he was German and told him that I was American, we switched to English. I mentioned that I traveled in the same manner and we talked about motorcycles for a while.

He told me that he was traveling around the world, and I heard about some of his experiences with the BMW on trains and ships. I remember that while we talked he pulled a valve spring out of his pocket and idly played with it. He told me of breakdowns and repairs: bearings in Singapore, accelerator cables in Israel, new brakes in Kenya, tires in Japan. When he had trouble on the road, he usually flagged down a truck and gave the driver a little money to take him and the BMW to the next town. In Mexico he had already cracked a piston, but was able to have it welded for a few pesos. He showed me his supply of spare parts, and also his rain gear, the best he could buy: special goggles, waterproof gloves, and a British-made rain suit. He hated helmets as much as I did.

I liked this man more and more as we talked. When he smiled, his eyes had the deep crow's feet of a man ten or fifteen years older, perhaps like the eyes of a pilot. He spoke with great affection of the places he had been and of the people he had met. For a few months he had worked in Australia to replenish his funds. In his wallet he carried a tiny map of Germany, with his home town in Bavaria marked on it. He showed the tiny map to me as he had shown it to many others all over the world.

We talked for a long time in front of the Cafe Habana. When I heard that he was on his way to Guatemala I gave him the names of hotels on his route, in Oaxaca, Tehuantepec, Tuxtla Gutiérrez, and San Cristóbal, and also some people to look up. He mentioned that the voyage from Panama to Colombia would be his fifth passage with the BMW on a ship. Before we parted he gave me his address in Germany and I gave him my address in California. I saw on the slip of paper that his name was Rolf. We shook hands and said goodbye and wished each other good luck.

Rum

Alcohol made a big difference after a long day on the road with the motorcycle. I remember arriving in Campeche, tired and sunburned after the 230-mile ride from Palenque. I found a hotel room, took a shower, then went out and bought a quarter-liter of Mexican rum. It cost less than a dollar. I found a little cafe that sold fresh-squeezed orange juice and took a table under a ceiling fan.

Twenty minutes later, after two big glasses of rum and orange juice, I felt much improved. When I left the cafe the sunset was just beginning. I walked along the seafront, watched the sun sink into the Gulf of Mexico, and then sat in the plaza until it became dark. Then I went back to my hotel room and slept for eight solid hours.

Safety

I saw quite a few Mexicans, mostly men, who limped or were disfigured in some way. Perhaps it is considered *macho* to be disdainful of safety precautions. Ceiling fans, for example, are often installed in hotel rooms where the ceiling is much too low. Several times I almost lost a hand while pulling off a shirt.

It is a common sight to see young men hanging from the open doors of buses as they travel in heavy traffic; in Mexico City I once saw a parked car that was half-crushed by a steel beam that had fallen from a tall building under construction; it is not unusual to see a large hole, completely unguarded, in the middle of a busy sidewalk; hoofed animals commonly graze within a few feet of the highways; women holding babies are seen riding sidesaddle on the backs of little motorbikes; and the men who make the fireworks for fiestas sometimes have cigarettes in their lips as they work.

Salt

Veracruz is not much of a town. I was there during the month of May, and it was also unbearably hot and humid. May is usually the hottest month in Mexico. It was so hot that I was taking cold showers, and I hate cold showers. I was taking three or four a day but it seemed to do little good. It was so hot that I literally could not walk around town, even if I kept in the shade and walked very slowly. At the cafes under the *portales* I had to reach slowly for my glass of beer or I would break into a sweat.

After two days of this I realized that my body needed salt. So I walked into a *farmacia* to buy a small bottle of salt tablets—what could be more natural? They had none. I tried most of the *farmacias* in downtown Veracruz, but none of them had salt tablets or had even heard of them. A couple of salesgirls gave me funny looks, as though I was some kind of salt fiend.

I left Veracruz and sweated even more in steaming Villahermosa, which could be the sweat capital of Mexico. No *farmacias* that I tried had salt tablets, and again I got funny looks from the salesgirls. "Take lots of salt with your food," one of them told me. In Villahermosa I remember seeing a restaurant that someone with a weird sense of humor had named the Cafe "Alaska".

Two days later, after a roasting-hot day of climbing around the Palenque ruins, completely drenched with sweat, I decided that it was a serious situation. I would simply have to make my own salt tablets. That evening I hunted around the town of Palenque for *cápsulas vacías* or empty gelatin capsules. Even they were hard to find, and it was in a veterinary pharmacy where I finally found them.

Afterwards I went into a cafe and ordered a cold bottle of beer—*bien fría, por favor*—from a young waitress. Then I spread a paper napkin on the table and proceeded to make a dozen salt capsules. I will never forget the look on the face of that waitress when she brought the beer and saw me filling those little capsules with salt.

San Cristóbal Part I

There is a general distrust of foreigners in San Cristóbal de las Casas, more than in other parts of Mexico. That part of Chiapas was only recently opened by road. But San Cristóbal is also a town where any anti-*gringo* feelings take second place. The principal conflict is the deep-rooted hostility between the *ladinos* and the Indians. It goes back hundreds of years, and much blood has been shed. Even an American can feel the bad vibrations in the town.

San Cristóbal has the feel of the highlands of Central America more than Mexico. It can be quite cold, even though it is about as far south as you can get in Mexico. There is a barrenness and sense of isolation which reminded me of Tierra del Fuego. For the person traveling alone, San Cristóbal on a cold and overcast day can be one of the loneliest places on earth.

San Cristóbal Part II

One time I was sitting on a low wall in San Cristóbal, on the active street between the market and the main plaza. A Mexican student was sitting a few feet away, his books next to him on the wall. I had already glanced at him unobtrusively, and he had probably done the same with me, but otherwise we ignored each other.

A steady stream of people passed by. I was interested in the different Indians who come into San Cristóbal from outlying villages. I liked the soft garments of white wool that were worn by many of the Chamulas; some of them wore black tunics or serapes that were also attractive. I especially liked the colorful ribbons on the hats of the Zinacantecans. Most of the Indians wore shorts, and because of all the walking that they do, many of them had great legs.

I continued to look at the outfits of the different Indians. Then an American girl appeared, with a lovely body, walking in a miniskirt and sleeveless jersey. This was better than any Indian! She passed the point where I was sitting. I watched her walk away, then suddenly turned to the young Mexican. He was looking at the girl also, and then he looked at me, and we both broke into big smiles.

Scissors

In the neighborhood of Calle Bolivar in Mexico City is a man who must be one of the finest scissor sharpeners in the world. The man is incredibly skilled, learned the trade from his father, has thirty-nine years of experience. Needless to say, it is not a simple matter to sharpen scissors. I watched him work on several types, including a tiny pair of cuticle scissors for a young woman. The man works with grace and flair, and it was a privilege for me to watch him. *"¡Una artista!"* I finally said in admiration. We had a brief talk about scissors after he finished sharpening mine. I remember that he said the scissors made in Germany were the best.

Second-Class Buses

I mostly rode first-class buses in Mexico. They are usually better, much faster, more comfortable, and almost as cheap. But sometimes first-class service was not available or was at an inconvenient time or the trip was short. I then rode second-class buses.

The great majority of Mexicans own no automobile and have to travel by bus. There are hundreds of independent companies that operate buses all over Mexico, regularly traveling into even the most remote villages. The second-class buses are quite cheap and relatively efficient. The low cost in pesos-per-mile makes it one of the most inexpensive ways to travel in the world. Breakdowns are common, but somehow the Mexican mechanics keep the buses running.

When I lived in Mexico I rode the second-class buses many times, and it was often an experience. I remember goats in the aisles, rabbits underneath my seat, a piglet in the arms of the boy next to me, chicken wings beating against my head. The buses were usually crowded, and sometimes I had small children sitting on my lap.

Second Time

In Mexico I observed an interesting phenomenon that took place at *loncherías,* taco stands, market cafes, *torta* shops, and other places where I would eat. The first time they saw me in those places I was a *gringo* and therefore cause for some apprehension. A *gringo* was highly unpredictable, often spoke weird Spanish, was liable to make unusual requests and behave in strange ways.

If it was a good place to eat I would often come back, and many times I noticed how much smoother and more relaxed it was the second time. They had seen me before and I was not quite so strange. Sometimes I would get increased portions or there would be some kind of friendly little act as a gesture of recognition. They seemed happy to see me come back, and of course it was also a compliment for them.

Señor Mendoza

One time I was waiting around in a tire-repair shop in Zamora while they put a *parche* on my motorcycle tire. The owner of the shop, a big man named Señor Mendoza, was smiling and friendly, and he started talking with me about Texas. He had a brother there, and his brother had told him that the Mexicans were not treated well in Texas. When Señor Mendoza gave me some details, I told him that I was not from Texas, that I was from California. He then mentioned the thirty *braceros* who had been killed on a bus in the San Joaquin Valley in California, an accident which had made headlines all over Mexico. Señor Mendoza was smiling and very friendly during the entire time he talked with me. When my tire was ready he charged me three times what the job was worth.

Serenata

The *serenata* is a public concert that is usually held in the main plaza of a town on Sunday evenings. I liked *serenatas* and must have gone to forty or fifty of them in Mexico; it is often the best place to be at that hour. All the people of the town can attend, and there is an interesting mixing of social classes and types of people.

The best time of the *serenata* is actually the hour before, as the plaza becomes more active and gradually fills with people. The evening is only beginning and there is a feeling of expectation. If the timing is right, the hour before the *serenata* will coincide with the sunset. These are unforgettable hours of the Mexican week, and it is a good time to sit in the plaza. My favorite place was usually on the eastern side, facing the west, so that I could also watch the sky change from day to night.

It is the custom for entire families to attend the *serenata*. The Mexican children usually look their best on Sundays, and I remember that it was a delight to see them walk by with their parents. After the music began I also liked to watch the young people walking around the plaza. The teenage girls often walk arm-in-arm, which I think is a pleasing sight. It is a diversion to observe the young people meeting; in Mexico it is sometimes the beginning of a courtship and an eventual marriage. One time I saw two teenagers, both very attractive, who had just paired off. They were shy and embarrassed and not even talking; the girl was blushing, the boy looked as though he was in physical pain.

It is sad to think of the less-attractive girls who come to the *serenata* every Sunday, week after week for years, and are never approached. I suppose that after a while they begin to stay home on Sunday evenings. In Mexico the status of being an old maid begins as early as twenty-two.

The high point of the *serenata* is after the town band has arrived and is setting up. The men smoke, talk among themselves, and are in no hurry to begin. I was often amused at their casual attitude. The *serenata* itself is not much; as I said, the best time is the hour before. Unless I was with someone, I seldom stayed for more than a few selections by the band. After the young people and strolling couples had come around two or three times, I usually lost interest and left the plaza.

Small Boat

Mexico has almost six thousand miles of varied coastline. Many of the fishing villages are isolated by unpaved roads or no roads at all and have never been visited by tourists. Some of the coastline is lushly tropical, with interesting lagoons and jungle-lined rivers that teem with birds and other wildlife. There are fabulous unvisited beaches, and in many places the fishing and shellfish collecting is excellent.

Views of the land from the sea have always appealed to me. Although it is about seventy miles away, I understand that the snow-capped volcano Orizaba, the highest peak in Mexico, is seen on clear days from fishing boats off Veracruz. I myself remember the lovely view of the Nayarit coast, as seen from beyond the surf at San Blas. There was a long palm-lined beach, an area of green jungle, and then impressive mountains rising in the distance. It is easy to imagine the same views as seen by men from sailing ships, as early as the 16th and 17th centuries. How exciting it must have been, after a long voyage, to see the tropical coast! At that time much of the land was still unexplored.

Ever since I read *Sea of Cortez* by John Steinbeck I have dreamed of seeing Mexico from the viewpoint of a small boat. I would explore the entire coastline, visit the small islands, do a lot of skindiving, see the fishing villages, look at all the lagoons, swim and sunbathe, do much fishing and shellfish collecting, take trips up all the rivers. The adventure would probably take two years and would surely be a great experience. My ideal companion would be a young woman who was a photographer.

Small Boys

On the second day of my trip to Morelia I felt that the motorcycle was not running smoothly, so I decided to stop in the town of Zitácuaro to check the timing and ignition. After I parked the motorcycle in a good spot and set up my tools, I noticed that two small boys had paused to watch me work. Soon there was a circle of fourteen boys—I counted them—watching me. There was not a word out of them, not a single question. But after a while they began to point at various parts and talk quietly among themselves.

When a *paleta* vendor approached I said, *"Muchachos . . . ¿quieres paletas?"* Several of them nodded gravely. The vendor gave them each a *paleta* and I paid him, for fourteen *paletas*. He was very happy with the big sale and decided to stick around.

After a few minutes I took a break from my work and sat down on the curb. I noticed that the *paleta* vendor was a good-looking young man. He smiled and said hello to the passing girls, but they all ignored him. We talked for a little while, mostly about the United States. Before he moved on he gave me a free *paleta*.

Spanish

Before I went to Mexico I studied Spanish for about two months. I studied it on my own, for perhaps an hour a night, with a Spanish grammar, a phrase book, a paperback dictionary, and a set of language records. These were no time-consuming classes. I learned right in my own apartment, which is really the most efficient way.

Learning a language is not very difficult. It requires thinking and concentration, but it is still a relatively low-level mental activity. It mainly takes time and effort. I was strongly motivated to learn Spanish, which helped considerably. I was excited because my trip was coming up and actually looked forward to studying every night.

By the time I crossed the border in Nogales I knew something about the language but had no experience in speaking it. I remember that it was a great thrill for me, during those early weeks and months in Mexico, to learn to speak Spanish. I was learning a language in the best way: not in a classroom back in the United States, but in specific situations in a foreign country.

It was also great fun. The learning process began as soon as I crossed the border, with the road signs: *Despacio, Puente Angosto, Poblado Proximo, Cuidado Con El Ganado*. In towns I would go out for a short walk and pick up five or six new words. I needed no dictionary for most billboards and advertisements: *Adelante* . . . . *Ahorre* . . . . *Goce Vida* . . . . *Tome Pepsi* . . . . *Corrida*. The meanings were easy to figure out. I also needed no dictionary for signs outside stores: *Joyería, Refaccionaría, Almacenes, Panadería, Novedades, Ferretería, Abarrotes, Peluquería, Zapatería*. I would just look inside and know what the word meant.

The Spanish words and phrases that I learned at first were entirely practical. They were what I needed to get along in Mexico, for travel and everyday living. During the first few days I concentrated on the nouns I needed in hotels, restaurants, and gas stations. I would write down words like *oil, tire,* and *sparkplug* and later look them up in my dictionary. I needed the word for *tablet* in the drugstore, *receipt* in the hotel, *stamps* in the post office. After learning all the food words I soon had no problem with menus. I looked up useful words like *truck, shirt, market, building,* and *newspaper* and rapidly built up my vocabulary.

The dictionary, by the way, contains some interesting

titbits: *bicho*, insect or vermin (not to be used in Puerto Rico) . . . *coger* (not to be used in Argentina or Uruguay). But the dictionary does not say why. Naturally all the Spanish obscenities, some of which are very colorful, are omitted from the dictionary.

Many of the Mexicans, including the women and children, swear like sailors. I sometimes heard *hijo de la gran puta,* which means "son of the great whore". The Spanish word for *fuck* is no doubt the most common obscenity. I must have heard twenty different forms of this flexible and all-purpose word. It is used in ways unimagined by grammarians. *Cabrón* is also very common. Since I was not fluent in Spanish, I never used obscenities in Mexico. I figured it was too risky.

Many times I wished there was a Mexican-American dictionary for people like myself, rather than the standard Spanish-English dictionaries. I wanted the words used in Mexico, not the ones used in Spain, Puerto Rico, or Argentina. I also wished there were Mexican-American phrase books and self-study books. What is wrong with the New York publishers, anyway? There is a large market for these books.

When I settled in the village I continued to study Spanish for about an hour a day. I made vocabulary lists and lists of useful phrases. The radio was an excellent aid, and I also read children's books in Spanish in the *biblioteca*.

The Mexicans were always very helpful. For example, one time in Culiacán I needed a fan for my hotel room. When I described it with sign language to the desk clerk, he told me the word was *abanico,* then he had me pronounce it until I got it right. I often made terrible mistakes in Spanish, such as confusing *jamón* and *jabón,* which are the words for ham and soap. Once I needed a light bulb and asked for a *globo de luz* because I did not know the word was *foco*. But the Mexicans were admirably restrained. They never laughed at me, and many times I was surprised at how quickly they figured out what I wanted.

In conversations with the Mexicans I soon learned to avoid

complete sentences, the kind that are given in textbooks. Instead I often used a questioning attitude and spoke in single words, phrases, and sentence fragments, which is the way people speak anyway. I found that my hands and facial expressions were very useful.

My recognition vocabulary became quite large, but my speaking vocabulary stayed relatively small. In time I became fairly skilled at nonverbal ways of communication, using gestures and expressions. It is amazing how effective these methods are, and with them I could understand and communicate much more than I could actually speak. With the Mexicans, almost better than fluent Spanish is the ability to communicate friendliness and good will, mostly in nonverbal ways.

I had thousands of conversations in Spanish with Mexicans of all ages, and some of the most delightful talks were with children. Perhaps they also took pleasure in having language superiority over an adult. It was a small boy in Amecameca who taught me how to pronounce Ixtaccíhuatl: Eeks-tah-SEE-uatl.

All the Mexicans were superior to me in the language. All women were eloquent. Every Mexican, even the little children, was a teacher. For me it was a country populated with professors of Spanish.

Language study works both ways, for there are always many Mexicans who are studying English. I once was friendly with a young secretary in Mexico City who was attending English classes in order to get a better job. Luisa helped me with Spanish and I helped her with English. We had a mutually beneficial relationship, based upon sex, companionship, and language practice.

The Spanish language is sometimes amusing. One of the names for the raccoon is *osito lavador,* which roughly means "little bear washer". The literal translation of the Spanish word for peacock is "royal turkey". And the literal translation of one of the terms for sanitary napkins is "little hygienic pillows".

It gave me a fine feeling to observe my knowledge of the language improve, to be able to handle more and more situations. Eventually I was able to understand about half of an overheard conversation on a bus; I could read the newspapers, although with some difficulty; and I could talk with a Mexican for twenty or thirty minutes before I felt the strain and became fatigued and started to repeat myself. From my notes on the process of learning Spanish, I see that I learned most of it during my first three or four months in Mexico, and then I reached a plateau. Apparently by that time I had learned as much Spanish as I actually needed.

Spotted Cats

There are three species of spotted cats found in Mexico: the margay, ocelot, and jaguar. All are primarily nocturnal and will probably not be seen except in zoos. The margay is very rare, but the ocelot and jaguar are abundant enough to be hunted. I cannot understand how an American hunter can shoot one of these beautiful animals. He would have to be of the same sick breed that shoots polar bears from airplanes.

I saw fine specimens of margays, ocelots, and jaguars in both the Tuxtla Gutiérrez and Chapultepec Park zoos. The margay is the smallest, about the size of a domestic cat, and is my favorite. I remember standing in front of the margay cage in the Tuxtla zoo for a long time and just responding to them. It is surprising that some entrepreneur has not started breeding margays, with the idea of selling the kittens for pets.

In tropical areas I sometimes asked the Mexicans about *tigres*. "Are there jaguars near here? Where are they?" Etc. etc. It is a good way to get the Mexican men talking, for in this respect *tigre* is almost a magic word. The eyes of the most reserved man would light up and he would begin to jabber away. The Mexicans have all heard many stories and legends about the *tigre,* and I think the big cat is the most interesting wild animal in Mexico. It is said that jaguars frequent the seacoasts to look for sea turtles laying their eggs. What a fine sight it would be to see a jaguar emerging from the jungle onto a moonlit beach!

Street Sights

Seen through an open doorway, a girl hand-painting piggy banks; she is surrounded by dozens of piggy banks, both painted and unpainted . . . . A man working in a store window who is making little animals from molten glass . . . . Mexico City: three Indians from the country, dressed in white, wearing *huaraches,* visibly nervous, staying close together; it is probably their first visit to the capital . . . . In 100-degree heat, a young man drenched with sweat as he struggles to remove a bus tire . . . . Painted on a wall: "Socialism is the end of the exploitation of man" . . . . One of the most common sights in Mexico: a shopgirl sweeping the sidewalk with a broom . . . . A poster warning against marijuana, calling it *El Tabaco Negro del Diablo* . . . . Two Mexican generals in sunglasses . . . . An Indian woman nursing her baby while sitting on the curb . . . . Street musicians: one man with a guitar, two with violins . . . . Outside a church, a group of little girls in white First Communion dresses . . . . A sign advertising a *gran baile* or big dance: *caballeros,* 25 pesos; *damas,* a smile . . . . A bent-backed shoeshine man in Mexico City, about sixty years old, with *Justicia Social* on the back of his shirt . . . . In a schoolyard, a pretty teacher refereeing two rows of boys as they play Grab-The-Scarf, a game that is fun to watch . . . . A beggar with only stubs for arms playing a harmonica . . . . Women working in a *tortillería* on a hot and humid day, their blouses soaked with sweat . . . . The old models of American cars that are no longer seen in the United States . . . . A taco vendor and a *paleta* boy making an even trade, a taco for a *paleta* . . . . In a

store window, a brand of pantyhose called *Dorian Grey* . . . .
A man walking with a cage of yellow-headed parrots . . . .
Legless beggars skateboarding through traffic . . . . A big man
with huge hands, intently reading a tiny photo-novella . . . .
The streets of downtown Mexico City, almost completely
white after a hailstorm . . . . A young American couple in a
four-wheel-drive vehicle; it is encrusted with mud and
carries gasoline cans and two heavy-duty spare tires . . . . A
cluster of urchins, mostly shoeshine boys, watching TV in a
store window . . . . Bored-looking girls and women standing
in line outside a *tortillería* . . . . A street magician surrounded
by a crowd . . . . A parking-lot attendant in Mexico City who
is also selling puppies and ice cream . . . . A pretty teacher with
a group of schoolchildren . . . . Painted on a wall: "PRI, the
party of the rich/Do not vote/*Viva* (a guerrilla leader)" . . . . A
mother and child walking hand-in-hand, both of them
barefoot . . . . A pig tied to the top of a second-class bus . . . . A
woman beggar with horrible leg-sores buying something
from a blind vendor . . . . A man with an ocelot kitten for sale
. . . . Schoolboys playing a quick game of soccer in the street,
using piles of books as goal posts . . . . A nun carrying two six-
packs of Coca-Cola . . . . A cafe owner bargaining with a
small boy for a basket of red snappers . . . . The open door to a
gynecologist's waiting room, filled with expressionless girls
and women reading magazines . . . . A goose in a tire-repair
shop . . . . A man in Mexico City riding a bicycle in heavy
traffic, balancing an enormous basket of rolls on his head . . . .
Inside a cafe, full-grown men watching animated cartoons on
TV . . . .

Street Snacks

The most tasty food I had in Mexico was not just from the
small restaurants and the *loncherías* and the cafes in the
markets, but also from the sidewalk stands and the street

vendors. Perhaps it would be an Indian woman, sitting on the curb with a charcoal brazier, selling strips of grilled meat; or a girl with a big can of steaming tamales; or a man behind a counter, rapidly making many kinds of tacos to order; or a group of food stands that specialized in *enchiladas con pollo;* or a woman outside the market with a portable stove, making *quesadillas* and frying them in a big skillet; or a *torta* shop with a window open to the sidewalk.

Occasionally I would find a *torta* shop that made exceptional *tortas* or Mexican sandwiches. The best ones contain unusual ingredients, and are often grilled or heated in some way. Naturally I would go back to these *torta* shops many times if the sandwiches were really good. My favorite was the *torta* made on a grilled roll with chorizo and avocado. When this sandwich is made right, it is delicious. It makes a good snack with a bottle of cold beer.

Eating at night can be a problem for an American in Mexico; many of the cafes and restaurants are almost deserted and not very appealing. Occasionally I discovered a restaurant that served a *comida* throughout the early evening, a great find for an American, but unfortunately these places are rare. The sidewalk stands and street vendors were generally the most common way I ate at night in Mexico. These entrepreneurs often did a brisk business; the food was usually good, and along with the high volume and low overhead, the prices were rock bottom. Fast food is just as appropriate to Mexico as it is to the United States, but in Mexico it is usually homemade.

Tacos from street vendors with carts were one of the most common things I ate at night. It is necessary to be selective: I would first look at the meat that the vendor had, perhaps watch him make a taco for someone, and then decide. I ordered just one, to see how it tasted; if it was good I could always order more. I learned that it is usually the custom to pay at the end, after you have eaten the taco. Often I said *Muy sabrosa* to the vendor after eating a street taco or something else. Those two words were much appreciated, and elicited many smiles.

In towns there is often an assortment of street vendors in front of the local moviehouse at night. The steps of the moviehouse are also a good place to sit and eat. In Mexico City there are numerous cafes, most of them open until late, that specialize in *caldo de pollo* or chicken broth. Tortillas and *caldo de pollo* with garbanzo beans and chicken livers added is very inexpensive, and is enough to make a light meal.

In tropical areas there are delicious snacks made from shreds of coconut that are sweetened with molasses and then baked. Sometimes they are sold by children carrying the trays on their heads. Once in Culiacán a boy sold me one that was still warm; his mother or someone else had just taken them out of the oven. I never did find out the name for these snacks, but this one was chewy and indescribably good. I followed that kid for three blocks, buying one after another.

I thought it was fun to walk around in the evening and sample the items from the different stands and vendors. It was entirely random, I never knew what I was going to eat. I would wander about, see what looked appetizing, and make my purchases. The best sign was a crowd of people around a sidewalk stand or street vendor. I delighted in the encounters with the Mexicans during these little transactions; I liked the exchanges in Spanish, and it was fun to go through the little rituals and courtesies.

Streetcars

One of the distinctive sounds in Mexico City is the sound of the electric streetcars. I overwhelmingly prefer these vehicles to buses: the riding comfort is greater, they are quieter, they are electric and therefore non-polluting. Streetcars have a surprising number of other advantages, and I look forward to the time when they make their reappearance in American cities. The windows of the streetcars in Mexico City are usually open; riding them is very pleasant, and a good way to see things. Several times I rode the different streetcars all the way to their terminals in the outlying districts, took a long walk, and then rode back again to the center of the city.

Susie

I soon discovered that the children of Americans who live in Mexico are often fluent in Spanish. Many of them are at just the right age to learn a foreign language. When I lived in the village I remember asking such children a number of times how to say something. They were rather good teachers, as I recall, and eager to be helpful. In addition I enjoyed very much the spectacle of being instructed by an eight-year-old child.

I also liked to talk with the American children about Mexico and ask them various questions. They often had keen observations and poetic phrasings that I could get from no adult. I heard numerous schoolroom tales, priceless descriptions of teachers, sensitive accounts of their small Mexican friends.

In the village there was one little American girl named Susie who would actually seek me out to give me Spanish lessons. She was eight years old, a blonde-haired little martinet, depressingly fluent in Spanish, who exploited her superiority over me in the language. Susie would sit me down in the plaza and have me go through drills, often the irregular verbs. Sometimes I was not in the mood for such demanding mental effort, which was usually combined with snide remarks about my Spanish. When I spotted her in the village I would often walk the other way or duck into a *tienda* before she saw me.

Tacos

I forget many of the important buildings in Mexico City, but I remember where to get the best tacos. There is one area where about a dozen taco stands exist within two or three blocks. It is a classic free-enterprise situation, with vigorous competition producing low prices and high quality. The tacos sold in this area are generally better and more varied than those to be found elsewhere. People come from all over Mexico City, and the taco stands are often crowded, especially at lunchtime and during the early evening.

The tacos are all made to order. When you have worked your way to the front of the crowd and it is your turn, you call out the type you want and then watch the taco man make it with great speed. The tortillas are soft, not hard as in the United States. Most Americans have never tasted a real taco.

The taco man puts sauce on it, rolls it up, wraps it in paper, and hands it to you. It is all done with flair, and the price is very low. My favorites were the *taco de puerco,* which is roast pork, and the *taco de barbacoa,* which is usually barbecued lamb. I remember that they were especially delicious at one stand. If I were to fly to Mexico City tomorrow, I would consider going directly from the airport to that taco stand.

Tamale

One time I was sitting in a sunny doorway near the market in Oaxaca. It was a cool day but I was comfortable sitting in the sun. There was much activity around the market and I was watching the passing people. After a while I noticed that a number of them were eating tamales. I figured that the tamales must be good if so many people were eating them.

I got up and managed to trace the stream of tamales to its source. It was a teenage girl, wrapped in a worn and shabby *rebozo,* standing by a large metal container. I indicated that I was interested in a tamale and she took off the lid, letting clouds of water vapor rise into the cool air. *"¿Verde, rojo, o dulce?"* she asked. I bought a *rojo,* walked back to my sunny doorway, stripped the corn husks off the tamale, and ate it. As I expected, it was very tasty.

Tapachula

It was the height of the rainy season at the time that I was returning to Mexico from a trip to Guatemala. A bus driver or *camionero* in Tapachula told me that the road to Tonalá had been washed out in two places and would not be passable for several days. I had learned in Guatemala that checking with the drivers at bus stations was a good way to find out the conditions of the roads, as they drove over them every day. I did not want to wait, so decided to put the motorcycle and myself on the train. I had ridden the Mexican railways several times before and had found them to be a good way to travel.

There was one train a day on the narrow-gauge line from Tapachula. For some reason I was late, and the train was filled and puffing when I arrived at the station. Three *equipajeros* hurried to help me lift the motorcycle into the baggage car. The conductors scowled at us, playing their *macho* role, and looked repeatedly at their watches. Everyone was looking out the open windows, and there was also a large crowd standing around. It was like the scene at the departure of a refugee train.

When the motorcycle was inside the baggage car, the *equipajeros* assured me that they would safely secure it. I was a little worried, because it is not easy to tie down a standing motorcycle inside a jolting baggage car. I wondered if the *equipajeros* knew how to do it properly. But the train was about to leave and I could only hope that they would do a good job. I thanked them for their help, gave them some money for *cerveza,* and then went into one of the passenger cars. Everyone looked at me, the American who was late and almost held up the train.

During the trip, which was only about 130 miles, I spent most of the time standing by the open windows on the platform at the end of the car. The conductors usually do not care if you stand there, although it is against the regulations. Most of them are very casual about it. In a typically Mexican way, they shrug and figure that if you get hurt it is your own fault.

This train, like most of the others I rode in Mexico, had a group of soldiers aboard. I knew they were not soldiers in transit, but were there to maintain order and protect the train. It is not unusual for Mexican men to carry guns on certain train rides; I have seen the guns. When you observe the rugged and isolated terrain in some places, this is no surprise, for there seems to be no law. I often wondered why murder and robbery were not more common.

The old narrow-gauge train was very slow and slowed down even more to go through the small villages. It seems that almost everyone turns out to watch the passage of the daily train. It must be a major event in their day. I remember looking at the staring faces and trying to imagine life in a small village on a tropical coast.

The train stopped in some villages for ridiculously small amounts of freight. In one place it was two baskets of avocados. I liked getting off the train at these stops, even if only for a minute or two. Some of the barefoot children stared at me as though I had come from another planet.

In the town of Pijijiapan we stopped for five minutes, and I had time to go to the baggage car to check my motorcycle. I saw that it was safely secured, the *equipajeros* had done a good job. The motorcycle was tied down with light rope, next to some crates of chickens.

When I got back to the passenger car, food vendors were thronging alongside the train, reaching up to the windows. I bought a *tamale verde,* a cold bottle of beer, and a few of those tiny bananas. The bananas are called *Dominicos* in most parts of Mexico and are very tasty. They are highly perishable and not often available in the cities.

Afterwards I resumed standing by the open windows at the end of the car. It was a hot day and the breeze was delightful. On one side of the train were the green cloud-tipped mountains of Chiapas, on the other was the coastal strip bordering the Pacific Ocean. As the train approached Tonalá it passed through miles of tideflats and lagoons, and I remember that I saw many species of aquatic birds.

Teenage Daughter

Hundreds of times in Mexico I helplessly responded to a delectable but unattainable Mexican female. I especially remember one time in a restaurant in Querétaro, where I could not concentrate on the *comida* I had ordered. Sitting at a nearby table was a luscious young girl with six or seven members of her family. She wore a white blouse, had long brown hair, and was about sixteen years old.

I traded many glances with this girl and several times caused her to smile. The Mexican girls often delight in playing little games with the eyes, and she was no exception. Her stern-looking father eventually noticed what was happening and looked over at me. Like most Mexican parents, he probably had the quaint notion that his lovely daughter should sleep alone. But from what I saw in her eyes, she was no longer just a schoolgirl, she was older than her father thought. I would have bet that she was already a young lady. From where I was sitting I could observe the rising and falling of her breasts as she breathed. Every time the nipples almost touched the edge of the table.

Tehuantepec

Tehuantepec is a disappointing place. It compares very poorly with the nearest attractions, the city of Oaxaca and the state of Chiapas. Most travelers regard Tehuantepec only as convenient for an overnight stop. Probably I have been there at the wrong time of year, but in my memory the Isthmus is a place of heat, dust, and strong winds.

In the Tehuantepec market I saw a woman who must have weighed four hundred pounds. I swear she used two stools to sit on, one for each massive buttock. I would have given anything to see this *Tehuana* bathing in the river with the other girls and women. It was easy to imagine her rising up out of the water, glistening like a hippo.

Tequila

It was in a village on the west coast that I met Anne and Cindy. We were staying in the same rambling, one-story tropical hotel, and their room was a few doors away from mine. They were both in their early twenties and had spent the winter skiing in Colorado. Anne was from Connecticut and Cindy was from Indiana.

One evening, after spending most of the day at the beach, we found ourselves sitting in the plaza. There was a full moon and the girls were restless. They wanted to drink some tequila, so we walked over to a liquor store and shared the cost of a half-liter. It was about two dollars. We then needed salt and limes, which are very necessary when drinking tequila. There are many variations in the drinking procedure, but the salt is usually licked first. The limes, if sucked quickly after drinking the tequila, will kill the awful taste.

Since the market was already closed, we had to go to a restaurant. Anne went inside because she was blonde and the sexiest and the most attractive. After a minute or two she came out smiling, with some salt in a paper napkin and a few limes cut in quarters. I could see the owner of the restaurant beaming from inside, and Anne told us that he had not charged her anything.

We walked away from the center of the village until we came to a quiet street, more sand than pavement, with palm trees and little houses. We picked a good spot and then sat down on the curb, with me sitting between the two girls. Only two or three people walked by in the half hour or so that we were there, and they paid no attention to us. We drank almost the entire half-liter of tequila, passing the bottle back and forth, licking the salt and sucking the limes. The three of us became quite bombed, there was much kidding around and hilarious laughter. That night with Anne and Cindy was one of the finest times I ever had in Mexico.

Terry's Guide

The book that is now called *Terry's Guide to Mexico* has had a long history. It had its beginnings as a slim volume published in 1909 by T. Philip Terry. It subsequently was revised and expanded and went through many editions. The original book is still good reading, but is now a collector's item and very difficult to find. An inter-library loan is usually necessary, but even then the book is sometimes too fragile to lend.

Here is part of a description of Córdoba in the state of Veracruz, written more than sixty-five years ago by T. Philip Terry: "Most of the houses are low and are roofed with red tiles which form a pleasing contrast to the luxuriant green of the tropical vegetation. The roofs are the favorite promenades of splendid peacocks. Somnolent *zopilotes* (buzzards) constitute the street-cleaning department . . . . Many of the old residents assemble here [under the *portales* fronting on the plaza] and take the rest-cure throughout the drizzling days. To the sound of squawking parrots they sit around metal tables and smoke cigarettes, criticizing the doings of the *metropolitanos* at the capital, swap discarded political ideas, play dominoes, re-clothe jokes that came over with Cortez and sip claret diluted with seltz-water squirted from blue-glass syphons encased in wire network. The general atmosphere of this region is hazy and lazy . . . .Córdoba recalls to mind the querulous traveler who complained that 'there was nothing to see and they wouldn't let him see it!' "

The author of the current edition of *Terry's Guide to Mexico* is James Norman. There is much to praise in this book. I think it is rather well-written; the prose is far superior to that of the other guidebooks. Considering that a comprehensive one-volume guidebook to Mexico is an extremely difficult task, *Terry's Guide* is a remarkable achievement.

The book is valuable for many reasons, including the descriptions of the land, the cultural and historical notes, the high level of taste, and the attention paid to the flora and fauna. The author has a fine sensitivity for the outdoors and natural beauty. Unfortunately there is much space devoted to sport fishing and big-game hunting. In my experience these pursuits often attract a type of ugly American to Mexico.

On occasion, during the description of a town or hotel or restaurant, a little bitchiness pops up in the book. I found these lapses delightful, and completely understandable as evidence of the weary-traveler syndrome. My heart goes out to the writer of a guidebook to Mexico. It is staggering to think of the work that is required, of the unattractive places that must be visited. Can you imagine having to check out the hotels and restaurants in *all* the border towns?

The hotels listed are mostly out of the range of the budget traveler, and for this purpose the book is of little value. In addition, the country-gentleman tone is sometimes annoying to the reader who is young and traveling with limited funds. At times the book seems to be written for the middle-aged and affluent, for the bourgeois traveler who must always have the best. One suspects that many years ago, perhaps as a child, the author traveled first class with his parents on a transatlantic liner, and it made a deep impression on him.

Sometimes the author portrays Mexico as seen through rose-colored glasses. In parts I thought, "This is propaganda …he writes as though he is a publicist for the government." In the section devoted to the history of Mexico, there is not even a mention of the recent massacres and political disturbances. The book could almost be stamped for approval by the Mexican government. I think part of the explanation for this is that the author lives in Mexico and is presumably a realist.

In the book there is an attitude of almost total acceptance of American imperialism in Mexico. The author seems unaware of recent developments in Latin America, of the profound changes that will inevitably take place. In another regard there is a willingness to parrot the official explanations of the Mexican government. One has the feeling that the author is friendly with some of the rich and powerful of Mexico. It is easy to imagine him as a guest at the hacienda of the governor of a state. I suspect this is part of the reason that his social-economic-political viewpoint is a lofty one.

One of the strengths of *Terry's Guide* is that the author has included much about the ancient civilizations of Mexico. In one part he describes how the Maya architects, instead of building rectangular courtyards, would have the side walls closer together at the rear, in order to create an effect of greater depth. In addition: "When there were long horizontal lines such as the steps of temples, they made the lines slightly convex in the center to overcome the illusion of sag." And I love this bit: "Throughout the course of his busy day the Aztec gentleman took time to sniff blossoms, just as we pause to smoke or take a coffee break. Flower-smelling was an important element in the cultivated man's education."

There are lines in *Terry's Guide* that some readers will find humorous: "Vitamin B_1 is said to drive away mosquitoes, but it also makes you smell like a circus lion . . . . Though the highway traverses flat country, drive cautiously because the road bed occasionally sinks . . . . The rooms themselves are rather poor, but the rats and mice do not seem to mind . . . .

Archaeologists have found evidence of the earliest cultivation of corn in the New World, dating about 5000 B.C. The ears of corn were about the size of a cigarette filter."

Here are part of the directions for getting to the famed Maya ruins of Yaxchilán in Chiapas: ". . . Take the Sureste Railway to Tenosique, Tabasco, and from there fly to Agua Azul, a lumber camp on the Río Usumacinta. From Agua Azul you take a dugout canoe downriver about five hours. The trip is like a Conradian experience, drifting through primeval silence, broken only by the chattering of monkeys, the bark of a jaguar, and the cries of jungle birds."

Tlatelolco

This area is on the north side of Mexico City and is now called the Plaza of the Three Cultures. In 1968, when I was living in California, I read in the newspaper about a massacre of students and demonstrators that took place there. It was not long after the more-publicized killings in the Zócalo. The official death count at Tlatelolco was something like 48.

Six years later, when I was traveling in Campeche, I had a conversation with a Mexican student. She told me there were tanks and machine guns at Tlatelolco, and that hundreds were killed. *"Los mataron . . . más de trescientos."* Many of them were students and young people. Then in Mexico City I met an English journalist who told me essentially the same story. The real account of Tlatelolco never appeared in the foreign press, only the official report of 48 dead. "We were not allowed to file," he said.

These accounts started me asking questions about what really happened in Mexico during 1968. I heard many rumors, tall stories, exaggerations, and conflicting accounts. "Tlatelolco stories" are what they are sometimes called. Many of the Mexicans and foreign residents were curiously close-mouthed about the subject, and a few seemed to be offended that I had even mentioned Tlatelolco.

I listened to the stories and then asked questions afterwards. Much of the information was unreliable. It was based upon second-hand or third-hand accounts and had to be modified or discounted. I was told that many leftist students had to leave the country or go underground; that the student left was traumatized by such a bloody act of political repression; and that as many as 1200 might have been killed over a period of time.

There is a Metro stop at Tlatelolco, and I once took a trip up there to look around. It is difficult to imagine the blood, the tanks and machine guns, the soldiers carrying away the bodies to be burned. I still would like to read a believable account of what happened in Mexico during 1968. For my purposes it should be from the point of view of a foreigner, and preferably an American. The whole area is properly the domain of a good investigative reporter.

Tomellín Canyon

The train ride from Oaxaca to Mexico City is supposedly a fifteen-hour trip, but the second time I took it, the train was an incredible ten hours late. The reason was a number of small rain-caused landslides in the scenic Tomellín canyon. I did not mind too much that the train was delayed, because I had a good seatmate and was also sitting next to a large window that could be fully opened. The rugged and isolated Tomellín canyon has much to offer, in particular a large amount of giant cactus. But a young man from Sweden was sitting in the seat behind us, and he could not believe it. "In Sweden," he told me, "when a train is thirty minutes late, it is printed in all the newspapers."

Tourist Towns

I could not understand the objections I heard everywhere to tourist towns in Mexico. You would think my fellow travelers were talking about lepers or criminals instead of people like themselves. In my experience tourist towns were welcome places, especially when I was on a long trip and had my fill of the Mexican culture. There were Americans and Europeans in these towns.

The main things wrong with tourist towns were the following: a greater concentration of irritants such as beggars, hustlers, *chicleta* boys, and serape sellers; the presence of numerous gift shops in the center of town; a significant number of townspeople who had been corrupted in various ways by the tourist trade; the offensive sight of the worst kinds of tourists; a shortage of accommodations at certain times of the year; overpriced and tourist-ridden cafes in the most popular locations; and sometimes higher prices for food and hotel rooms.

Except for these characteristics and a few more, the so-called tourist towns were just as Mexican as the others. Sometimes there were even more Mexican and Latin American tourists than people like myself. It is easy to avoid certain things, for example the tourist cafes and restaurants. Numerous low-priced eating places, patronized by the townspeople, are always located within a few blocks of the main plaza. These towns even have certain advantages over the others. The people are used to tourists, for one thing, so you get stared at less. Many of the Mexicans have learned to speak Spanish more clearly and slowly with foreigners. Some of them have acquired a real interest and curiosity in the varied travelers they meet, and are more open and friendly.

Travel Fatigue

I sometimes traveled in Mexico for extended periods of time, and on these long trips I eventually became very tired of it all. I became tired of being cheated, of fumbling with Spanish, of being a conversation piece, of people always trying to sell me something. American women told me they became deadly tired of coping with the advances of the Mexican men.

When traveling on long trips I often felt a strong desire to hear English spoken. I was actually lonely for the language, and have stood close to people that I did not want to meet just to hear the sound of English. A few times, after speaking nothing but Spanish for a week or more and then seeing Americans in a town, I almost jumped into their arms.

This urge to be with other Americans or English-speaking people usually coincided with a general depression. It often happened when I was sick, or when I was near the end of a long trip, or when it rained constantly, or when it was very hot, or when something unfortunate had happened. Occasionally all these things happened at once.

I remember that I would become very tired of all the stares from the Mexicans. I wanted more than anything to speak English with people like myself. Suddenly I would become acutely aware of all that is fourth-rate in Mexico. I would routinely check the *cines* for American movies, I even had strange desires for ice-cream sodas in American-style restaurants.

I have talked about this state of mind with other Americans who were traveling in Mexico. Sooner or later it seems to happen to almost everyone. We generally agree that it can be a combination of many factors, among them bad luck, homesickness, and travel fatigue. In addition it is a reaction to the strangeness of Mexico and a longing for our own language, culture, and society.

Traveling Alone

Because a motorcycle should only carry one person on long trips, I did not have the option of traveling with someone. I traveled alone on my trips in Mexico. But I met people everywhere. These people, some of whom are described elsewhere in this book, were my only companions. They brightened many an evening and rainy afternoon, often in remote and out-of-the-way places.

In general I prefer traveling alone to traveling with another person. There is no question about it: I meet more people, I have a better time, I see more. For me the main advantage of being alone is having an unfettered consciousness. There are other advantages, too. When I traveled alone in Mexico I had much closer contact with the Mexicans and was forced to speak more Spanish. I lived from day to day according to my moods and did whatever I felt like doing. My plans and commitments were minimal, I had maximum flexibility and freedom.

Tropical Fruits

In the different markets I visited in Mexico, I always kept an eye out for tropical fruits. They interested me for reasons I still do not fully understand. I looked not only for my favorites but also for new ones I had never seen. It was sometimes confusing, because there are many varieties of these weird-shaped tropical fruits, and they usually have a number of names. Indian vendors in remote areas will often not know the Spanish name for a fruit, they will have a name of their own.

When I returned to Mexico City from my motorcycle trips, I looked up the fruits I had encountered in a reference book. It was *A Manual of Tropical and Subtropical Fruits* by Wilson Popenoe (New York, 1920). There may be a better or more recent reference book, but that was the only one available in the Biblioteca Benjamin Franklin in Mexico City. The book has photographs, good drawings, and a certain amount of charm. I became rather fond of it. In regard to the names of fruits, Popenoe says that a fruit of tropical America might have forty or fifty different regional names.

I suppose that my favorite tropical fruits in Mexico are the Manila mango, the cherimoya, and the *zapote chico*. The mango and *zapote* are described elsewhere in this book. When the cherimoya is at its best, it is surely among the finest fruits in the world. I cannot understand why it is not exported to the United States. The pitaya is another strange-looking but tasty fruit that is worth mentioning. The pulp and seeds are often combined with sugar, water, and ice to make a refreshing drink in the *tierra caliente*. It is important to remember that all these tropical fruits are seasonal and vary widely in quality; to encounter them at their best is a privilege.

Tropics

One time I was leaning in a doorway in a village on the coast of Nayarit. It was during the rainy season and I was watching the afternoon shower beat down on the palms and thatch roofs and tropical vegetation. I had been there for about ten minutes, released from my activity by the sudden downpour. The rain was a predictable event that occurred every afternoon, and I knew it would not last long.

I could see a sow and several piglets in the bushes across the way, foraging for food and oblivious to the rain. Most of the pigs in the village wandered about at will and ate almost anything. The roast pork was probably delicious. Above the sow and the piglets was a mango tree, heavy with ripe fruit. The animals were undoubtedly rooting for fallen mangoes.

That part of Mexico, like others I had seen, was as tropical and beautiful as anything the South Pacific has to offer. The rain began to let up. I remember that a teenage girl walked by, too wet to care about the rain, her bare feet splashing in the puddles. I could see that her soaked blouse was clinging nicely to her breasts.

Trucks

I saw Mexican truckdrivers most often in the cafes along the major highways. Just as in the United States, several trucks outside a highway cafe means that it probably is a good place to stop. The Mexican truckdrivers looked to me like very decent men. A few times I was invited to sit at their tables and talk with them. I was a curiosity: an American traveling on a motorcycle, and sometimes in a remote area. The men always wanted to know where I was from and where I was going; without exception they all wanted to know how much the motorcycle cost.

I had long ago noticed on the highways that many of the Mexican trucks approaching me in the other lane had names painted on them. They were painted somewhere on the front of the truck, most often on the bumper, and usually with the same funny-looking style of lettering. The names were either about the driver or the truck itself, sometimes it was hard to tell.

I liked those painted names, which were often humorous. They personalized the truck in a way that is not done in the United States. The *camaraderie* among the drivers was also made stronger, for the trucks could be easily recognized. On long stretches of highway it was a diversion for me to read the names as the trucks approached. Some of the ones I translated and wrote down were: *The King of the Neighborhood, I Sinner, My Blue Prince* (a truck that is painted blue), *Little Angel, Barrabas, The Centaur of the North, Marco Polo,*

Black Dog, My Pretty One, The Grand Prince, Pampas Bull, Bogart, and *Almost an Angel.*

Tuxtla

Tuxtla Gutiérrez is a busy and unpretentious commercial town, the capital of the state of Chiapas. Few tourists bother to stop there, they usually continue on to San Cristóbal de las Casas. But I liked Tuxtla, found the *Chiapanecos* to be self-assured and friendly, and stayed there for several days. Tuxtla can be hot, but I am told that it is seldom humid. The area near the main plaza is a great place to be as the town cools at dusk, especially on Sunday evenings when there is a *serenata*.

The state of Chiapas is one of the leading producers of coffee in Mexico, and much of it goes to Tuxtla Gutiérrez for distribution. I remember a *cafetería* there that I much preferred in all of Mexico. It not only sold coffee wholesale and retail, but also by the cup. There were several tables provided for this purpose.

When I entered this *cafetería* I would immediately smell the aroma of roasting coffee. The two ancient coffee-roasters were in plain sight, and once I observed how the roasted beans were removed and the green beans put in. I would drink my coffee at one of the tables—somehow it tasted better in this place—and occasionally hear the sound of coffee being ground. An attractive young woman worked behind the counter; I remember wondering if her body smelled of coffee. Coffee beans were sometimes on the floor of this place, and piled against the wall were burlap sacks of coffee with CHIAPAS stenciled on them.

Tuxtla Gutiérrez is the location of the *Instituto Botánico de Chiapas*. It is an interesting place to walk around, for all the different palms and tropical trees are labeled with their names. On the main floor inside the building is a large relief map of Chiapas, with the vertical scale much exaggerated.

The map is color-coded and shows the different vegetation zones of this fascinating state.

Tuxtla has one of the most pleasant zoos I have ever seen. It is small, just the right size to see in one visit, and specializes in regional birds and animals. At this zoo I saw a baby tapir, with the characteristic streaks and white spots; a pair of newly-born peccaries, very small as they stood beneath their mother; and a coati-mundi in one of its characteristic sleeping positions for the daytime: it was curled up on the floor of its cage, with its eyes covered by its front paws.

In the Tuxtla zoo when I was there was a fine specimen of a harpy eagle. No one else was near its cage, and I was only six feet away from the huge bird. Roger Tory Peterson, in his *Field Guide to Mexican Birds,* describes it as "very rare; reported Veracruz, Chiapas, Campeche. Habitat: tropical forests." I remember that I looked at this magnificent bird for a long time. It stared back at me with its great eyes and fierce-looking expression. The harpy is one of the largest eagles in the world, with powerful feet for catching sloths and monkeys.

Urban Buses

A ride on an urban bus in Mexico can be exhilarating, for they are sometimes driven at relatively high speeds. The drivers are very casual about it and do not seem to be worried. I suppose some of them figure that all the religious junk they have displayed will protect them. The buses hurtle along. If they are old, they make a great racket. The speed appears to be higher because of the cobblestones and unrepaired pavement and narrow streets. It can be a hair-raising experience, and I was often gripping the bar of the seat in front of me.

The drivers sometimes do not make complete stops. To save time and a downshift, they often like to have you step off while the bus is still moving. It takes a little skill, and I thought it was fun. When I stepped off an urban bus in Mexico, hitting the street on a light run, I sometimes had the same feeling as at the end of a roller-coaster ride.

Uruapan

On Sunday evenings the plaza and *portales* in Uruapan are crowded with people who come in from the surrounding countryside. I am told that they come from all over that part of Michoacán. Along with a number of other towns in Mexico, the *portales* in Uruapan shelter food stands that are open at night, and sometimes rather late. These places are a real find, especially for an American. They usually provide chairs or benches around a common table. The specialty I remember is *enchiladas con pollo,* where pieces of pre-cooked chicken are sautéed with several types of vegetables and then served with enchiladas.

One night in Uruapan I was having this tasty and inexpensive dish at one of the food stands under the *portales.* It was during one of the heavy rains that are frequent in Michoacán. The air was chill and damp, but I was warm enough in a sweater under my *manga.* The food was hot and there was also a little warmth from the charcoal stove. I still remember the honest face of the Mexican woman, lighted by the fire as she did the cooking for her circle of customers. They seemed to be mostly people who had come in to Uruapan from the surrounding countryside and had to stay overnight.

The woman was assisted by a small girl who was probably her daughter. I liked the way I seemed to be accepted by the circle of people. It was also a mild example of primitive comradeship: we were all sheltered from the rain, huddled close together and eating *enchiladas con pollo.* A passing *borracho* started to ask me for money, but one of the men turned and said, "Don't bother him, please" in Spanish. It is highly unusual for a Mexican to intervene in such a manner, and I thought about it afterwards.

Vast Slums

For a number of reasons I had more good moods and states of euphoria in Mexico City than in any other place I have lived. Being unattached at the time, I had all the leisure time I wanted. I remember that several times I was on a bus in Mexico City and for various reasons was very happy. Perhaps I was sitting next to an open window and the route was also stimulating. So instead of getting off at my intended stop I rode the bus all the way to the end of the line.

It was in this way that I saw some of the vast slums that exist on the fringes of Mexico City. What I saw has been reported and needs no description here. The scenes, however, reminded me of the Italian films made after World War II, the so-called "neorealist" films. The best example of this genre is probably *The Bicycle Thief*.

Village Part I

It is not so easy to live in a Mexican village. The new resident from the United States will see that it is a continual learning process, with many surprises. A large amount of practical information must be acquired, for things that are simple and easy in the United States are not always that way in Mexico. One thing I soon learned is that instead of going out to buy something, I often went out to have it made.

Unless you speak fluent Spanish or are something of a hermit or desire total immersion in Mexico or are part of a group, an American must usually live where there are a number of English-speaking people. This fact is sad but true. If you don't believe me, settle in a village that is totally Mexican and see how long you like it.

For most people it is unwise to stay too long in a Mexican village. The reason is basically a matter of diminishing returns. Although a few stay for years or even a lifetime, the optimum length· of residence for most people is less than three months. After that the lack of activity and stimulation becomes a real problem. That is one reason why a Mexican village is a good place to finish up a creative project, but not to begin one.

An American should have meaningful work to do in Mexico, and maintain a discipline. It is not enough to be an artist or writer. You must have multiple interests and activities, for it is a very long day in a Mexican village. You will work hard and do a number of things and relax and talk with friends and read and write letters and still have several hours left over. I found that a box of books from the United States was an absolute necessity. Another good idea was to use the village as a base and take a series of trips to other parts of Mexico.

Village Part II

There was already an enormous cultural gulf between myself and the people in the village, but I did what I could to minimize it. I learned Spanish well enough to carry on a conversation. I generally conformed with the Mexican social customs and rules of decorum, and always used the elaborate Spanish manners. My appearance was usually that of a student living on a subsistence income: this helped, for it minimized the economic difference. I did nothing to threaten the cultural and social values of the Mexicans in any way. I tried to treat everyone in the village with courtesy and respect, which is actually very easy to do, for such an attitude seems to be built right into the Spanish language. After a while the word evidently got around the village: for a *gringo*, he is all right. Once I overheard two people in the market talking about me, and it was very gratifying to hear the word *simpático*.

Village Walk

I left the house and started walking towards the plaza . . . . Stopped to look at the new *tortilladora* that the women are talking about. The owner was there, happy and beaming, a successful Mexican entrepreneur. He is proud of his new tortilla-making machine, and he knows it is going to make him rich. It is new, and it squeaks, and it is funny-looking, but it steadily produces thousands of tortillas every hour . . . . Saw a milkman going from house to house, his burro loaded with sacks of milk . . . . In the open window of the candle-maker's shop I watched the oldest daughter making candles. The method they use is an iron ring, six feet in diameter, with about fifty candles hanging from it. We talked a little, she used *tú* with me for the first time . . . . A little boy came by with a tray of that caramel-flavored candy on his head . . . . At the main intersection a policeman was directing traffic. In a Mexican village a policeman is often cheaper and less trouble than a traffic signal . . . . Walked past the window of the local photographer. On display are portraits of Mexican children, dressed in Sunday clothes, holding large crucifixes and trying to look devout . . . . I leaned in the open doorway of the carpenter's shop and watched him work on a coffin. In his shop there is always a good smell of wood shavings and pine boards . . . . I watched the arrival of an ancient second-class bus, filled with *campesinos* coming to market, sacks of foodstuffs tied on the roof . . . . A baby burro . . . . Next to a jacked-up bus, a man was repairing a hole in a tire. In the United States the tire would have been thrown away . . . . Bought a half-kilo of *carne de planada*, listened to the weird

sound as the butcher took the meat and proceeded to flatten it
. . . . I watched a sidewalk vendor doing a brisk business with
a wind-up toy. *Campesinos* and Indians from the hills stopped
and gaped. I imagined the scene that night in an outlying
village, when a wife finds that precious pesos were spent on a
frivolous toy instead of an essential . . . . A man walked by,
carrying a small pine coffin on his shoulder . . . . I stopped to
watch two masons, father and son, working on a wall . . . .
Around the corner came a slow-moving group from the
cárcel, shepherded by a policeman, back from a few hours of
labor repairing the streets . . . . I walked past a school, heard
the voices of children singing from within, stopped and
listened for a minute or two . . . . Picked up a copy of the
Laredo *Times,* had a nice exchange with the newsdealer I
walked past the *panadería* and smelled the aroma of baking
bread . . . . Watched a man paste up a *futbol* poster, then read it
. . . . I saw a pretty teenage girl braiding the hair of her
younger sister . . . . Saw two burros loaded with firewood . . . .
I passed the doctor's daughter outside the *banco.* We
exchange smiles and hellos now. I waited for her to give the
greeting first and then said the same, as she knows what is
most appropriate. This time it was *buenas tardes* . . . . Picked
up my mail at the *correo,* headed for the plaza . . . .

Volcanoes

The first time that I took the train from Oaxaca to Mexico
City, it arrived in Puebla just before sunrise. The conductor
told me that the train would be in the station for fifteen
minutes, so I had time to go out on the platform for some
coffee. It was winter in Mexico and rather cold at the 7000-
foot altitude. While I shivered in the cold air on the platform
and warmed my hands with the hot coffee, I looked up
and suddenly saw the two volcanoes, Ixtaccíhuatl and
Popocatépetl. They were clearly visible to the west.

It was a magnificent sight that I will never forget. The sky was deep blue in the cold air, with a few rose-tinted clouds from the sunrise. The Puebla station was still in shadow, but a line of sunlight was now about halfway down the volcanoes. The two snow-capped peaks were clear and bright in the first rays of the rising sun.

Walking

We who normally live in the temperate zone must change our way of walking when we travel in the tropics. There is a technique to walking on the hot streets and not working up a sweat. I followed the example of the Mexicans and walked very slowly, keeping in the shade at all times. I also used a kind of mental control. In general, the hotter it was, the slower I walked. Several times on the Gulf coast, where it can also be very humid, I was almost walking in slow motion.

Washstands

The first washstand I ever used was in a one-hotel town in Jalisco, about two weeks after I entered Mexico. I remember seeing the washstand in my hotel room and thinking, "What is that thing for?" Then I found out that the rooms had no running water. In a typical American way I was annoyed at the backwardness of the Mexicans. I had no choice but to stay in the hotel and use the washstand, for it was almost sundown and I had been on the motorcycle all day.

I looked at the washstand without enthusiasm, but resigned to using it. There was the usual metal stand with an enamelled basin and pitcher, a soap dish, a towel bar, and a pail below. At least the towel was clean and white. I had seen washstands in movies, usually westerns, but had never used one. At that moment I needed directions of some kind, perhaps a pamphlet entitled "How to Use a Washstand." I could not ask the maid, for she would think I was an idiot.

The next morning I shaved with it for the first time. To my surprise it was highly efficient. Not only that, but it was actually fun to use. Less than one and one-half quarts of hot water were needed. The basin was exactly the right size. I realized that washstands had been around for a long time, and the most efficient design had already evolved.

I began to like that washstand. It was so simple and functional, and above all it was minimal. In the United States I had always thought of running water as a necessity, but now I saw that it was only a convenience. A source of water is all that is really needed.

Afterwards I used other washstands in different parts of Mexico. They are quite common in rural areas. Some of the roadside cafes provide washstands, which are often placed outdoors; I remember the delight of washing up in brilliant desert sunshine. I have seen washstands strongly made of bent and welded steel rods, the kind that are used to reinforce concrete. I have seen others that are almost antiques, and marvelous to look at. Eventually I came to greatly appreciate washstands. The simple act of washing up became a graceful and almost monk-like ritual. There were times when I looked at washstands and just admired them for what they represented.

Watching Them

The Mexicans are surely among the fastest and most coordinated people on earth, and take great pride in their work. I was always watching them. Even the small children could do so many things that I could not do. The Mexicans knew how to do such things as herd goats, clean octopus, load burros, kill chickens, open coconuts, carry turkeys, catch iguanas, build huts, use machetes, slaughter pigs, find oysters, saddle horses, make *huaraches,* skin animals, and harness oxen.

Young Girls

In Mexico I paid special attention to the groups of schoolgirls in white blouses and short skirts that I saw on the streets after school was out. My favorites were naturally those girls in their mid-teens and older. I often admired the pleasing contrast of the white blouses with the tan and brownish skin. Many times I responded to the youth and beauty of these spirited girls, their shining hair, young complexions, melodic voices, and bright eyes.

Some of them had fully-developed figures, but still had to wear a little girl's outfit. Throughout Mexico I never tired of observing this phenomenon. I feel no guilt or embarrassment because of my response to these young girls. It is perfectly natural, the young females are prized in almost all cultures.

On national holidays in Mexico it is customary for these schoolgirls to march in parades, along with many other groups. I watched a number of these parades, usually standing in a doorway so that I could see above the crowd. To see these succulent sixteens dressed in short skirts and lined up in a military way, and marching in step to the music of a Mexican band, is a sight to behold.

Zapata

In books and museums I saw the old photographs of Emiliano Zapata, with that great moustache and those burning eyes. To me he is the most interesting and appealing of the revolutionary figures. I often wondered what the young Mexican leftists think of him, and would not be surprised if he was highly regarded. Zapata posters are sold in Mexico City and other places. His political ideas, especially in regard to the redistribution of land, were so advanced that I suspect the Mexican government is a bit afraid of his memory.

The prologue of *Zapata and the Mexican Revolution* by John Womack is good reading. It has personal information about Zapata as a man and describes how he was first elected to defend his village when he was thirty years old. Robert Millon, in his book *Zapata: The Ideology of a Peasant Revolutionary*, says: "According to those who knew him personally, Zapata was quite frank, simple, and accessible, and possessed great strength of character . . . he was always considerate with his followers and especially with the peasants, who almost venerated him. He had a great natural talent, learned readily and displayed rapid, almost clairvoyant insight into people and their problems; it was difficult to deceive him."

Viva Zapata! is a bad film with a hopelessly bad script that was once made about him. The film is a prime example of the Hollywood lie and must be terribly offensive to most Mexicans. I know it was offensive to me in a number of ways. Mexico and its people are depicted much better in two other American films, *One-Eyed Jacks* and *The Treasure of the Sierra Madre*.

Zapote

The *zapote chico* is one of the outstanding tropical fruits in Mexico, and I always kept an eye out for the little brown shapes when I was shopping in the markets. When they are properly ripe, they are delicious. I would actually keep them until they became slightly overripe, for the *zapote* is at its best when the skin is cracked and a little juice is oozing. Wilson

179

Popenoe, in his *Manual of Tropical and Subtropical Fruits,* likens the flavor to that of pears and brown sugar together, and it is a good description.

The *zapote* is also used to make an exotic and delicious dessert. An American woman whom I knew in San Miguel de Allende used to make it for her guests, and I was in her kitchen one afternoon and watched how she did it. As I remember, the fruit is mashed and strained, then whipped with lime juice and brandy. Possibly something else was added or done. The brown mixture is then chilled for several hours before serving, and it is fabulous.

Zócalo

The Zócalo in Mexico City is not a very interesting place. It is certainly not attractive, with its open, hard, and barren expanse, which is surrounded by monolithic buildings. It reminds me of *1984,* the futuristic vision of George Orwell. Although I have never been there, the Zócalo also reminds me of Moscow, perhaps of Red Square.

A hotel that faces on the Zócalo offers a view of the bleak scene from the veranda of a restaurant on an upper floor. There are *portales* on two sides of the Zócalo, oversized and not of human scale, but at least they provide shelter from the afternoon rains in Mexico City. Below the southeast corner is a group sculpture depicting the founding of Tenochtitlán. I think one of the figures, the Indian pointing with gaping mouth, is hilarious.

There is undoubtedly much to see in the National Palace, which faces on the Zócalo, but for some reason the building did not interest me. There is an authoritarian feeling to it, a hint of fascism in the air. The entrances to the massive and unattractive building are guarded by soldiers or military police with automatic rifles. Perhaps it was my imagination, for the bloodshed of the 1968 massacre was on my mind, but they seemed positively unfriendly. I remember an afternoon when I asked a teenage soldier where his attractive-looking weapon was made. He told me with a sneer and mock toughness that it was from Belgium.

Continuing around the Zócalo, the smaller church to the right of the cathedral has magnificent ornate facades. It is also partly faced with *tezontle,* a lightweight volcanic rock that has been used since the time of the Aztecs for buildings. I always liked the smaller church much better than the massive cathedral. Inside it is cool and quiet, and a welcome relief from the noise and traffic of the Zócalo. It is a good place for the traveler to sit and rest.